underground plant life

The Amazing World
Beneath Your Garden

Charles R. Self, Jr.

DRAKE PUBLISHERS INC. NEW YORK•LONDON

Published in 1978 by
Drake Publishers, Inc.
801 Second Ave.
New York, N.Y. 10017

Underground plant life

LC: 77-88947

ISBN: 0-8473-1667-X

Design: Raymond M. Sotnychuk

Printed in the United States of America

CONTENTS

Introduction / v

Chapter 1 / The Structure of Soil / 1

Chapter 2 / Soil Classification / 17

Chapter 3 / Soil Testing / 23

Chapter 4 / Soil Care / 32

Chapter 5 / Roots / 63

Chapter 6 / Plant Propagation / 74

Chapter 7 / Root System Problems / 94

Index / 101

INTRODUCTION

Though a book on the underground life of plants may seem too specialized to help the average home gardener, there are many points where no other type of information is more necessary to good growth of many, many plants. While the importance of leaf and stem growth is great, no plant survives without roots. With proper treatment of any root system, any plant that receives a reasonable amount of sunlight will grow healthily to maximum size, bloom, seed, fruit, produce vegetables, or otherwise fulfil its genetic heritage.

Often, all too often, a plant is placed in a spot in a house or garden where it gets maximum sunlight and is watered weekly, but is otherwise ignored. Most plants will actually survive under such treatment, but there is a great loss in the plant, for it does not, cannot, feed properly. With a few tests and a bit of quick formulation, you can add years to the life of some plants, make others bloom earlier, transplant with almost never a loss, get early blooming or ripening, and receive maximum enjoyment from all of your plants. A knowledge of root systems also makes plant propagation without seed a quicker and easier job.

All in all, there is much benefit to the average gardener in a reasonable knowledge of the underground life of plants.

Chapter 1

THE STRUCTURE OF SOIL

That handful of soil you pick up to check for moisture content when you are getting ready to prepare the ground for planting is not a simple inorganic glob. Within that handful you will find not only inorganic materials, but also organic materials, gases, bacteria and other microbes, larger animal and insect life, and many chemicals in solution. That handful of dust is, in a sense, both alive, and life itself. (Fig. 1-1)

The structure of all soils is moderately complex, and the process of soil formation, as well as the differences among soils, region by region, can be a source of fascination to all persons. The formation of the soil found in your region of the country is affected by the local climate as well as by the availability of the stuff from which soils are made, so that the variety is seemingly infinite over the face of the earth. Still, the classification of soils is possible, for there is a basic similarity from one to another, enough so that scientists have formulated systematic methods for determining just where on a list any soil made up of particular substances belongs. And that soil classification list is of great importance to farmers and gardeners, for it is there that soil preparation for good growth needs to start.

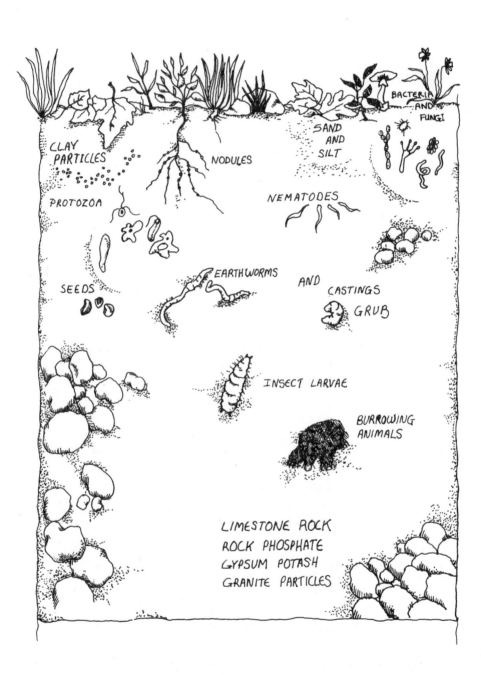

Fig. 1-1. Cross Section of a Handful of Soil

Mineral Material

Soils are made up essentially of two types of materials: those that are soluble in water and those that are not. Of course, there are also soluble and insoluble chemicals. Among the most common soil minerals are silicon, aluminum, iron. Trace elements, such as magnesium, often appear and are essential to healthy plant growth. Oxygen, though listed as a chemical and not a mineral, is also a major component of soils. Carbon, hydrogen, zinc, nitrogen, sodium, potassium, copper, and iodine appear in most soils in varying degrees, with varying effects on fertility and the growth of particular kinds of flora, or plant life. Soil minerals and chemicals are deposited in soil layers in many ways. Loose sedimentary layers may well weather and deposit their share, and the weathering of rocks will add to the accumulation.

Soil Water

Soil water differs markedly from the water we draw from our faucets at home, or at least it should. Tap water is expected to be a relatively pure form of hydrogen and oxygen, although, in actuality, there can be quite a concentration of minerals, chemicals, and bacteria in even the safest tap water. Soil water, however, is a carrier of most of the nutrients that sustain plant life. Good soil water in a fertile area will supply all the essential nutrients for plant growth in a form that allows the plant to convert, extract, and use the nutrients to grow and produce. Soil water, then, is a solution, and bears within it a loose conglomeration of many nutrients needed by plants. If the proper nutrients are abundantly available in soluble form, plants grow well.

Soil Water Types

Soil water begins with precipitation in any of its forms. As the water runs off or soaks into the ground, it picks up the necessary elements to provide nutrition to your plants.

Although soil water originates from precipitation, it takes different forms once it hits the ground. Gravitational water is water that moves downward through the soil, pulled by the force of gravity. It moves through the spaces between individual soil particles, with the downward passage continuing until the gravitational water reaches an area called the zone of saturation. Below this level, all the spaces between individual clumps of soil are already filled with water. The actual depth of the zone of saturation is determined by local conditions, with the strongest affecting factor being the amount of rainfall in an area.

Gravitational water is of great importance in many ways. It affects everything from the color and texture of the soil, right on up, or down, to its chemical composition. The action of this fluid moves the finer particles of topsoil with it, down deeper into the soil layers, some of the material being deposited at every step along the trip. This mixing and transportation of the soil materials can provide you with a good type of soil, with all the needed elements for growth, or it can, in extreme cases, build a clay hardpan once all the finer topsoil particles are carried deep beneath the surface.

Gravitational water can also strip a soil of soluble nutrients by leaching out chemicals as it makes its downward trip. This leaching action is the reason why farmers in certain areas, such as rural Virginia, are advised to lime their fields at least once every five years. If leaching continues unchecked, and the soils are not fed, then the topsoil will become stripped of all but the densest and least soluble minerals and chemicals. The process of nutrient loss may continue if the pressure within the zone of saturation becomes such that there is an actual underground water flow.

Not all soil water, as it passes on its downward course, makes it to the zone of saturation. Some gravitational water attaches itself by surface tension to particles of soil. This is capillary water. It serves as a reservoir of water-borne nutrients for the plants in the vicinity. Capillary water moves as water pressure dictates — from areas of more water to areas of less — and can be expected to move in any direction. If rainfall is sparse, capillary water will move sideways or vertically in order to reach plant roots. When this sort of movement takes place, the capillary water packs a liquid meal; included in the drink are nutrients that have been in the subsoil areas and now are brought back to the plant roots to sustain life. In some cases, though, the minerals and chemicals brought up from the subsoil are not exactly beneficial to the plants. Saline and alkaline deposits may remain after the capillary water is used by the plants. When lime is brought to the surface in this way, it can eventually form a hard layer almost like concrete; this caliche layer, as it is called, is much like clay hardpan and will serve to prevent the downward flow of rainwater into the soil.

Of little importance as a plant nutrient carrier is hygroscopic water. This is water bound to the surface of soil particles by a strong electrical charge. Hygroscopic water does not supply plants with needed water. Because it is bound, no movement is possible.

Soil Gases

Air in the soil is essential to the life processes of plants. It supplies oxygen and carbon dioxide needed for the various life processes that must take place. In some soils the space between particles may be so large that as much as 50 percent of

the volume is made up of soil air. This air differs little in composition from that which we breathe, though usually it has a
higher concentration of carbon dioxide, a bit less oxygen, and
a higher humidity. Soil gases are necessary to plant life processes. Few plants will survive where the ground is so saturated with water as to eliminate the pockets where the gases
accumulate and are available to the plants.

Organic Material

Organic material is the gardener's friend. Soil is made up not
only of inorganic materials and water and gases, but also of
humus. In addition, good, fertile soil teams with organic life.
Countless life forms, from tiny bacteria to good-sized moles
and other burrowing rodents will make their contributions to
richer soils.

Humus — organic material, plant and animal, that has been
broken down at least partially by bacterial action — is of great
importance to soil structure, since it provides a catalytic action
for needed chemical reactions by which plants extract nutrients from the soil. The humus also improves soil structure by
increasing the capacity for water retention and by restoring
minerals to the soil. In addition to these essential functions,
humus also serves as a food source for the wide variety of
microscopic organisms that live in soil. (Fig. 1-2)

Earthworms

The earthworm is a fine example of animal contribution to
plant life. Though its role in aerating and loosening soils is
well known to many gardeners, a review may be helpful.

In the temperate zones of the world there exist more than
a thousand varieties of earthworm. In the process of feeding,
these earthworms increase the number of fine particles in the

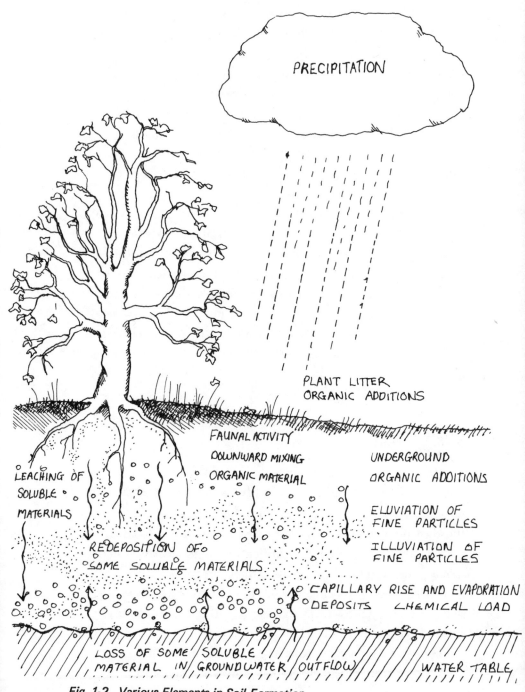

Fig. 1-2. *Various Elements in Soil Formation*

soil, and they leave castings — manure — that are richer min-
erally than the soil in which the earthworms feed. The average earthworm is said to produce its own body weight in castings in about twenty-four hours. And according to research
conducted by the venerable Charles Darwin, one earthworm
may pass through its body as much as fifteen tons of dry earth
each year. While producing these castings, the earthworm
may burrow as far as six feet into the subsoil, breaking up and
aerating it, making burrow holes that allow rainwater to penetrate it deeply and easily. And when they die, their bodies
provide a nitrogen-rich fertilizer for the soil.

The soil is always better for the action of earthworms, as
it is aerated and mixed and mineralized. In fact, the addition
of earthworm-laden compost is an excellent, efficient way to
permanently break up hardpan soils. Simply turn your compost and its load of earthworms under, and it will be years —
assuming enough organic matter is added to give the hardwork-
ing little invertebrates a decent start — before the soil repacks,
if ever.

Microorganisms

The flora of the soil comprehends many different microorganisms. Fertile soil abounds in such life. A few are large enough
to be seen with the naked eye, but most range in size from
those visible with an ordinary microscope on down to those
visible only by the intense magnification of an electron microscope. The system of which these microorganisms are a part
is enzymatic, and thus digestive. They act to break down resistant materials into forms that are useful to plants as nutrients.

Bacteria are present in soils in greater amounts than any
other organism: in a single gram of soil, you can expect to

find an average of one billion bacteria; and an acre-foot of soil (one acre of soil one foot deep) may have as many as a thousand pounds of bacteria! Bacteria serve to convert unavailable, or insoluble, nitrogen into forms useful to plants. The conversion starts when certain bacteria turn the nitrogen to ammonia, whereupon other types continue the process, which proceeds through insoluble nitrates to soluble nitrites.

Actinomycenes are near relations of bacteria, though more complex in structure. A few produce plant diseases, while many help break down organic matter and release mineral nutrients.

Phages and viruses form the smallest microorganisms, and they are *not* beneficial. Phages will disease the bacteria of the soil, and the viruses may cause diseases in higher plants.

Fungi can be found in soils in average concentrations of about a million per gram. Because of their much greater size, the poundage per acre-foot of soil may reach a full ton. Most fungi are beneficial to the extent that they help to decompose organic matter in the soil, but a few cause harmful plant diseases.

Algae, too, abound in soil. These microscopic plants produce chlorophyll and change carbon dioxide from the air into organic matter (but only in the presence of sunlight). The surface layers of an average soil may contain as much as 300 pounds of algae per acre-foot.

Protozoa are the simplest organisms actually classified by scientists as animal life. They are single-celled, microscopic creatures, though larger than all but a few types of bacteria. Basically, they serve the same purposes as do bacteria in building soils.

The activity of almost all of these microorganisms is affected by the soil environment. During cold weather most of the bacteria and other organisms are dormant, or nearly so. As temperatures in the soil approach 55°F., the microorgan-

isms begin to become extremely active, with maximum activity occurring around 85° to 90° F. Once the soil temperatures
exceed 100° F., however, the activity of bacteria and other
microorganisms will slow up or cease entirely.

Moisture is another factor affecting microbial activity. Very
dry soils show little sign of activity, and extremely wet soils
show distinct signs of a drop in favorable, active flora. In extremely wet soils, anaerobic organisms (those that grow in an
atmosphere lacking in oxygen) may take over, causing many
problems. Anaerobic organisms use up the soil oxygen, and
may convert nitrates into gaseous nitrogen sulfates and sulfides.

Aeration of the soil prevents competition among microorganisms for the available soil oxygen.

The acidity or alkalinity of soils is also of great importance,
for microorganism activity depends in large part on just how
far in either direction the soil goes. Control of the pH (the
measurement of acidity or alkalinity) is of great importance
in gardening and farming. We'll cover that subject in detail a
bit further on, under soil testing and improvement.

Soil Characteristics

The physical properties, or characteristics, of soils are extremely useful in describing them and in determining whether
or not a gardener needs to take corrective action, and, if so,
just what those actions should be.

Soil color is the most visible, though a long way from the
most important, of soil characteristics. The color of soils can
vary from near-white through browns, reds, yellows, greys,
and so on. Each color will give some clue to the properties of
a soil, but it will not provide anything like a definitive state
on how well crops will grow in the soil. Most people raised
in the temperate regions tend to think of a good soil as one
that is black with humus. Yet in many areas of the southern

United States — as I write, I am staring at a red clay cutbank in back of my house in rural Virginia — the soil is far from that classic color; its productivity is still as great as, or greater than, that of black soils.

Most humus is, in fact, black or brown, so that soils high in humus do tend to stay closer to those colors. As the humus content drops, the color will fade off to a lighter brown, possibly even grey. Red and yellow soils are often high in iron content, with the oxides providing the color scheme and the color of the contained humus often being overridden. In moist areas, light grey or white soils usually have little iron content, whereas in drier climates, white or light grey soils will usually have a high content of various salts.

Soil Texture

Soils come in different textural classes based upon the particle size of the minerals in the soil. Basically there are three types of particle — sand, silt, and clay. (Actually, the first class is gravel, but since arable land is seldom gravelly to a major degree, we ignore it here.) Sand is categorized as between 0.05 mm and 2.00 mm in diameter; silt is between .002 and 0.05 mm; clay is smaller than .002 mm.

From these measurements of particle size, a different classification of soils is derived, and it is the one most often used to describe the texture of a soil. This latter classification is based upon the combination of the different sorts of particles, that is, their relative preponderance of sand, silt, or clay. In general, there are three major classes: sandy soils, loamy soils, clayey soils. (Fig. 1-3)

In sand soil, silt and fine clays will make up less than 20 percent of the total weight of the soil, with the sand particles large enough to be visible to the naked eye and irregularly shaped. The water retention capacity of sand soils is low, but

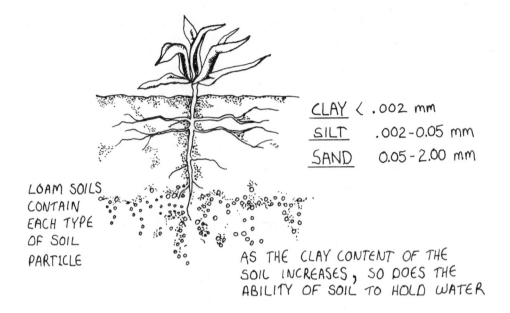

CLAY < .002 mm
SILT .002-0.05 mm
SAND 0.05-2.00 mm

LOAM SOILS CONTAIN EACH TYPE OF SOIL PARTICLE

AS THE CLAY CONTENT OF THE SOIL INCREASES, SO DOES THE ABILITY OF SOIL TO HOLD WATER

Fig. 1-3. The Three Basic Textural Classes of Soil

drainage and aeration are excellent. Sandy soils are usually found in a loose, easily crumbled (friable) condition.

Clay soils have particles that are extremely small, tending to the microscopic. The pores between particles are also extremely small, and have a large water retention capacity. Water and air move through clays extremely slowly. Clays have a plastic quality, tending to be moldable when wet, and to retain the molded shape when dry. When dry, they have strong cement-like qualities. Friability is usually poor.

Loamy soils are those that are most widespread in the United States and much of Canada, which is a fortunate occurrence for most of us who wish to grow anything of good quality. Loams are not as easily identified texturally as they fall about halfway between the sandy and clayey types. Generally, a loam soil type will have qualities of heaviness — clay — and lightness — sand — in just about equal amounts, which has the advantage of giving loam soils the good features of each type. Loam soils don't have the extreme looseness of sandy soils, yet retain much of the good water holding capacities of clayey soil. Loams don't become solid as easily as do clayey soils, so that air and water movement in the soil is freer and of more benefit to plant life.

Of course, the various loam soils will show features ranging from heavy clay content to heavy sand content, so that a true 50-50 loam is seldom found. Testing your own soil to determine its type is simple. Take a bit and rub it between thumb and forefinger. Sands feel coarse and gritty; clays are fine and sticky; silt, if dry, will feel "floury." If you are still in doubt about the exact composition of your soil, take a small sample in and talk with your county or other agricultural agent. These agents are invaluable in testing and determining a great many things for farmers and gardeners. It's probably past time you made the acquaintance of the person working your locale. (Fig. 1-4)

If your soil texture is one that can be classified as ideal, the particles will be rounded and will lie loosely in your hand, after being easily shaken apart.

For more accurate measurements, geologists classify clay soils as those having diameters less than 0.002 mm, silt soils as those with diameters from 0.002 mm to 0.05 mm. Sandy soils will have particles with diameters from 0.05 mm to 2.0 mm. Gravels are soils over 2.0 mm, and under 2.6 mm. There we leave soil classification, and go over into ground cover, classified as inert rock fragments.

Soil Structure

Soil structure closely follows soil texture, since the individual particles in each type of soil tend to clump in one manner or another to form masses. These masses are known as peds, and reveal the workability of a soil as well as its permeability and porosity. Soil structure is strongly affected by cultivation,

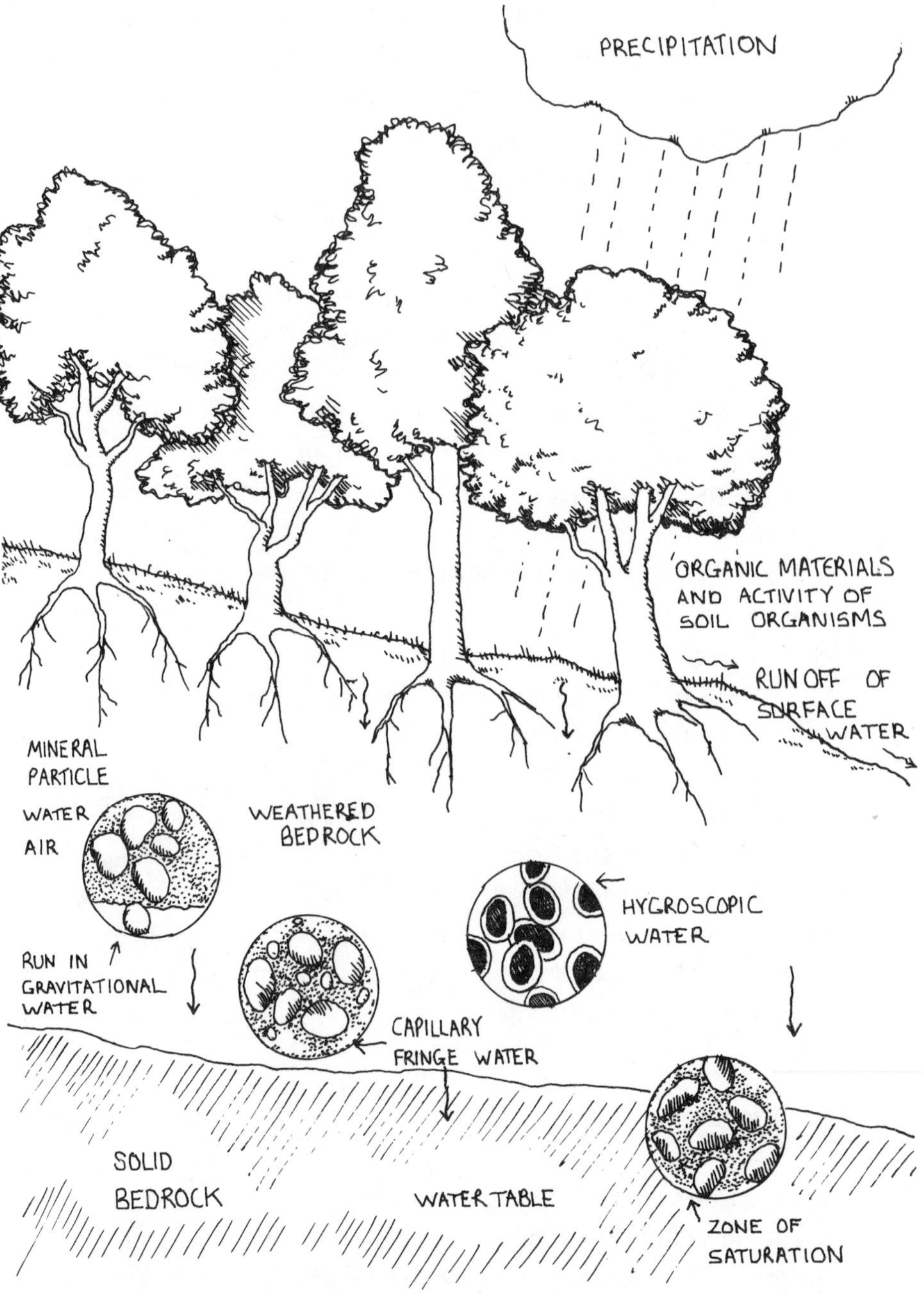

Fig. 1-4. Environmental Factors and Their Relation to Soil Formation

irrigation, and fertilization, as well as by the climate and the mineral content. (Too much sodium and magnesium in clay soils will provide you with nothing more than a formless sort of glue when it is wet.)

Soil Development

At one time this orb on which we stand, sit, ride, walk, waddle, cry, laugh, and jeer was nothing but one big rock, at least on the surface. As time passed, microbes of varied kinds were the only living things. These microbes liberated carbon dioxide, along with some types of acids in which rock is soluble. The rock started to break down. And as the microbes lived and died, they added organic matter to the minerals and chemicals formed by the dissolved rock. Climatic factors helped then, as they do today — expansion, contraction, cracked rocks. Organic life increased in complexity, living on the soil, adding to the layers of materials already present. As life on earth moved up the evolutionary scale, higher forms of plants, such as ferns, gained a foothold in the soil provided by earlier forms. As the soil base became suitable, even higher plant life forms evolved. (Fig. 1-5)

The biological, chemical, and physical process of soil formation takes a long time. Even today, with many higher forms of plant and animal life to contribute to the formation, it can take five hundred years to form a layer of soil a single inch thick. Considering how rapidly we have managed to destroy a good deal of the original soil cover around the world, that thought can prove a bit more than unsettling.

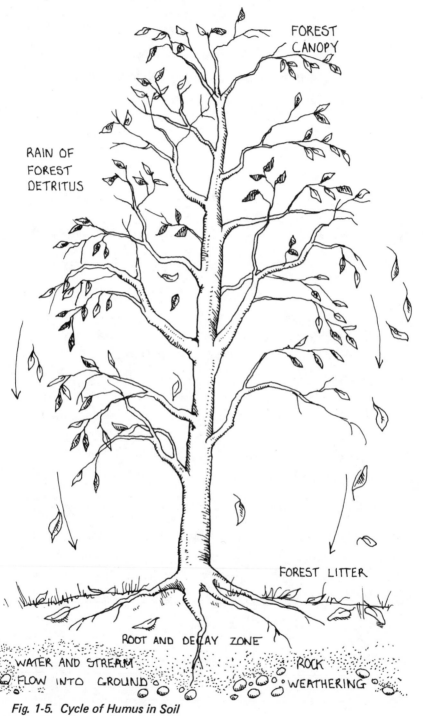

FOREST
CANOPY

RAIN OF
FOREST
DETRITUS

FOREST LITTER

ROOT AND DECAY ZONE

WATER AND STREAM
FLOW INTO GROUND

ROCK
WEATHERING

Fig. 1-5. Cycle of Humus in Soil

Chapter 2

SOIL CLASSIFICATION

There are several major soil classifications of importance to farmers and gardeners of the United States and Canada.

Prairie soils are found in those areas where no trees grew during the soil's formative period. Their organic content is high because of the tall prairie grasses that did grow. The soils are rich in humus, have a deep structure, and are usually not leached or calcified. This is of exceptional importance to us, for the *only* such area in the world covers nearly 300,000 square miles of the United States — most of Iowa, a lot of Illinois (possibly 75 percent), southeastern Minnesota, eastern Oklahoma, eastern Missouri, some of eastern Kansas, a bit of central Texas. The humus layers are as deep as 20 inches in a few sections, and rainfall averages about 40 inches a year. There is no extremely heavy hot weather rain to cause leaching.

Desert soils in the United States are found in parts of Nevada, Utah, Oregon, Idaho, and Washington, with some extensions into Texas, southeast California, Arizona, and New Mexico. Other portions can be found in western Colorado. Desert soils are found in arid regions where grasses will not grow. They are low in organic matter. Low rainfall causes a problem, with even semidesert areas having as little as 8 inches of rainfall per year. The land must be irrigated to be used for

17

crops, but it tends to be extremely fertile when this is done.

Chestnut and brown soils take in areas in the following states: Colorado, Idaho, Arizona, Kansas, Texas, Utah, New Mexico, Montana, Wyoming, Oregon, and Washington. Such soils were developed in grass-growing regions, though the grasses were shorter than were the prairie grasses. There is modest rainfall, usually not more than 15 inches per year. Irrigation is usually needed to produce good crops.

Adobe soils can occur in areas where the annual rainfall is less than 20 inches and seasons are clearly definable as wet and dry. Usually the soils are heavy clay types. These soils will need to have organic material added to them to produce crops, but the results tend to be much better than just good when this is done. Adobe soils are found in California, Colorado, Arizona, Texas, Nevada, Wyoming, Oregon, Utah, and New Mexico.

Rendzina soils are dark soils over particular types of limestone formations. Their humus content ranges up to a very high ten percent and the region will be humid. Soil color will be grey, brown, or black. Most rendzina soils in the United States are found in areas of Alabama and Mississippi (known as the black belt).

Bog soils are located in Illinois, Ohio, Wisconsin, Iowa, Indiana, and Florida, close to the areas in which those states usually have prairie soils. (Though bog soils can be located elsewhere, they are more likely to be found around prairie soil areas.) Peat soils such as this have an extremely high humus content, but they must be drained to produce crops.

Podzolic soils occur in temperate regions of high humidity, where forests once covered the land. The soils tend to be somewhat grey in color, though the variation is great. Since at one time much of North America, and probably half of the present United States, was once forested, this type of soil abounds. Organic litter will cover the top layer of soil — tree branches, leaves, etc. — with a partly decomposed layer under-

neath. Next will be a layer of black humus, and under that
will be the mineral soil. Podzolic soils are highly acid, and even
more so in those areas where coniferous forests once stood.
(Coniferous trees tend to greater acidity than do deciduous.)
Podzolic soils overlying limestone, though, are usually neutral;
maples and beech trees often predominate in such areas. Podzolic soils are found in New York, much of New England,
around the Great Lakes, down to about Tennessee, with some
running south into east central Texas.

Laterite soils occur, in the United States, in Mississippi and
Georgia, with some found in California (the far northern areas)
and Oregon. This type of soil is formed in areas where there
are, or were, heavy tropical forests and hot and humid weather. Rainfall can be no less than moderately high, with the degree of laterization increasing with heat and humidity. Having high concentrations of iron oxides, laterite soils are red,
though the actual topsoils may be brown or grey. The soil is
often crusted, and the heavy rainfall contributes to leaching.
Soil silica content will be low, which also aids the leaching
process. Basically, laterization means the production of a soil
high in iron and aluminum and low in silicon. Silica content,
in fact, may be as low as 2 percent, whereas iron and aluminum may make up 70 percent of the soil. Laterites are high in
insoluble phosphates. (Phosphate combines with the aluminum or the iron to become insoluble.) Rock phosphate fertilizers are usually necessary to prevent this combination and
provide free phosphate for plant life. The upper portion of
laterite soils will be loose, crumbly and porous, with strong
granulation. The soil is usually slightly acid, unless heavy rains
have leached out the calcium. Humus content is low, as it
breaks down rapidly under high heat, rainfall, and much insect activity.

Chernozem soils vary from dark brown to black, with the
brown chernozems being found more often in southern areas
of the soil's range. Lime content is high, and climatically the

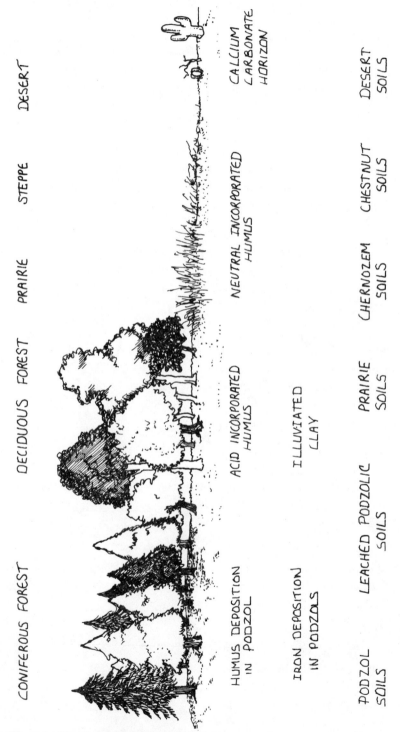

Fig. 2-1. The Areas in Which Different Types of Soil Occur

darker colors are simply found, which reacts with the soil make-up differently under conditions of heat as compared to cold, where there are extremes of heat and cold. Chernozems in this country are found in a wide belt across the Great Plains. Perhaps three-quarters of North Dakota is chernozem, while South Dakota is one-half, as are Nebraska, Oklahoma, and Kansas. Much of west Texas, some of eastern Washington, and a part of western Idaho are also covered with chernozem soils. The soil will range from neutral to a bit alkaline, as there is not sufficient rainfall to leach calcium from the soil. Aluminum and iron tend to remain in the topsoil, while most chernozem areas have a layer of lime a few feet below the surface. The chernozem areas are those of modest rainfall, seldom exceeding 27 or 28 inches per year, and occasional drought conditions are probable.

Classifying soils in this manner is at best an oversimplification. We should all remember that there are plenty of variations on each theme, and that frequently those variations may fall in geographical areas where they could be unexpected: certain mountain areas in the Northeast tend toward tundra soil styles, a type not covered in this book because there is so little of it in the lower forty-eight states. Desert areas actually are broken down into several different soil types, and the two found in the United States are officially classified as semidesert instead of full desert. (Fig. 2-1)

Still, the above distinctions will serve to give an idea of what the soil in an area is and how it got that way. Once that's done, a few relatively simple checks can provide us with just about all the information needed to provide plant nutrition of a type to allow maximum growth of most any type of flower, vegetable, tree, grass and so on down the line. A knowledge of the soil content can also make a crop choice much simpler: for example, podzolic soils are short of calcium;

many grasses require heavy doses of calcium for healthy growth, whereas most coniferous trees do not. It also becomes possible to check for the depletion of nutrients found naturally in particular soil types, so that, before even considering planting in an area, you will have an idea just how well or poorly the land has been treated over the years. And proper soil conditioning for good root growth cannot be overemphasized. Without the correct soil conditions, you might just as well spend your time at the neighborhood tavern as out in your garden, for the results will be very similar.

Chapter 3

SOIL TESTING

In general, four soil tests are performed to discover what soil nutrients are present, in what amounts, and to see just what must be added to condition the soil for the crops you decide to plant. This testing can be just as important for a single simple houseplant (or a less simple houseplant) as it can for a fifty-acre field full of potatoes. It is easily done by the home gardener or by a county extension or agricultural agent.

The four tests will show the potassium (potash) content, the phosphorus content, the nitrogen content and the pH or acidity/alkalinity level of the cropland (or flower pot). With the test kits available to the home gardener, you will note results that, except for pH, do not show the actual level of the particular nutrient. The test results will show instead *the percentage of deficiency.* This saves your having to make the conversion to percentages needed when working with fertilizers. When fertilizer is produced, it is bagged and labeled usually with some approximation of 5-5-10, or 10-5-10. Invariably, you will find those figures to mean the content of nitrogen (first number), the content of phosphorus (second number), and the content of potash or potassium (final number) in the fertilizer, whether it is organic or manufactured. Thus, when using the Sudbury soil testing kit, you simply match the color of the final test tube contents against the enclosed charts

23

and read directly the formulation you need to have a balanced series of meals ready to apply to your plants.

Measuring the acidity or lack of acidity of soils is a bit different. Here you will be working with the pH scale, a method of measuring hydrogen ions that indicates the level of acidity or alkalinity of the soil (potential of hydrogen is actually what you're measuring). This is expressed by means of a scale running from one to fourteen, with seven being neutral.

Acid soils run to the low side of the pH scale, while alkaline soils run to the high side. Most soils in wetter regions will be at least slightly acid, or sour, since rainfall leaches the calcium from the soil. In drier areas, soils will most often be alkaline, or sweet, though overliming in humid areas can easily produce an alkaline soil.

There is a great variation in plants as to requirements and tolerances of conditions. Most vegetable crops will do best in a slightly sour soil, that is, one where the pH is about 6.8 to 6.9, though blueberries and cranberries both prefer strongly acid soils. (Blueberries are among the strongest acid preferences of all, with a liking for soils as far down the pH chart as 4.0, while cranberries will not do well in a soil that reads higher than 5.0.) Almost no other berry or plant, of any kind, likes a 4.0 level of acidity: that is simply too strong, though the pitcherplant will tolerate that level, as will the aspidistra. Virtually no plants will thrive if the alkaline level rises above 8.0, though there are a goodly few that will at least tolerate this level. As you can see, then, there is a wide, wide swing in just this one soil feature, so that it is sometimes possible to select the crops to fit the soil rather than changing the soil to fit the crops.

There are two methods of soil testing. The first, and simplest, is to take soil samples from several areas of the garden and have them tested by your local agricultural agent. In most states, this service is provided free or at minimal cost, but it often takes a couple of weeks to obtain the results, particularly since most people are starting to test and getting ready to plant at about the same time, thus overloading the labs.

The second method is to do it yourself. For my own testing I prefer to use a Sudbury Soil Test kit. Get the size you feel you need. (Prices range from under $10 to over $50, and the cost reflects the number of tests possible with the kit.) The more extensive your garden, and the more testing you expect to do, the larger the kit will need to be, of course. I specify the name of the kit here only because I know of no other such kit on the market. As far as I know, the Sudbury kits are the only ones suitable for most people to use. They are specifically formulated to be easy to use and require absolutely no special knowledge, just a reasonable amount of care in taking the soil samples and doing the tests.

In addition to speeding results during the heavy testing season, a do-it-yourself soil-testing kit offers a second benefit. It makes it possible for you to secure periodic checks at times when you wouldn't be able to get samples to the local county agent in order to do serial tests. Such serial tests may be needed. Soil make-up generally changes on a yearly basis, but extra heavy rainfall and other factors can cause leaching and other problems, so that a garden, lawn, or orchard can change composition drastically in less than a season. Successive tests will reveal such changes and allow you to make the extra preparations needed to get maximum production and growth.

Taking Soil Samples

The selection of samples is probably the single most important part of soil testing. To ensure accuracy the tools and utensils used must be clean, of course; old dirt clinging to a trowel or a soapy film on a glass can badly contaminate the test results.

Now, take a series of soil samples, going at least three inches into the subsoil after cultivation, and no more than four or five inches in. If you are going to plant in a landfill area, you should take in the same areas, samples from a depth of one foot and two feet in order to get an accurate idea of total soil make-up. To get samples from that deep down, I recommend that you use a posthole digger. (Borrow one if you must.)

Soil samples should be taken when the ground is dry enough to be cultivated. If the soil is too wet to plow, it is too wet to provide good soil samples. If a damp soil sample is taken, it must be allowed to dry before the tests are made. Drying should be done naturally, since extreme heat, such as that from an oven, can change the composition of the chemicals present in the sample.

If more than one soil sample is taken, you will want to work out a method to keep them straight. Mine is simple and easy: I place a piece of masking tape with the data, such as "NW corner, 10 ft. inside fence," on the glass containing the sample. Some so-called experts recommend taking several soil samples from around the garden, then mixing them all together to get an average reading. This may be a superb method of soil testing if you're absolutely sure there is, for example, no limestone shelf that stops about halfway across the garden. Otherwise, you may end up with one end of the plot overlimed or overphosphated and the other a bit short of the needed nutrients. My advice is to keep the soil samples separate and take the few extra minutes necessary to make the multiple tests. It will pay in the long run. (You can go to mixed samples after you run the first couple of tests if all ends and sides of the garden seem to provide similar test results.)

Testing for pH

With the soil samples ready, you can now run the tests. Use a

clean test tube and fill it a quarter full of dry soil. Don't heat
the soil, and don't touch it with your hands. It is also a good
idea not to smoke while making these tests (in case you do
have a habit). Add some of the test solution, bringing the tube
up to half full. Cork the test tube and shake it vigorously. Let
the soil settle and compare the translucent fluid on top of the
soil with the color chart included with the kit. The color
won't match exactly. What you are actually looking for is a
color *density,* not a color, so matching in that manner isn't
important. If the color falls between two of those on the chart,
it is easy to estimate where it stands, because the color density will vary strongly to one side and not so strongly to the
other. (Fig. 3-1)

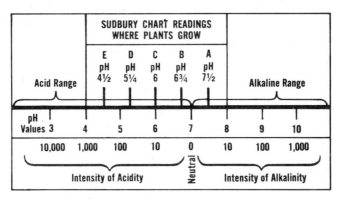

Fig. 3-1. Chart of pH Scale from Sudbury Soil Test Kit

Nitrogen Deficiency Testing

To test for nitrogen content, or deficiency, first fill a clean
test tube a quarter full with Solution 2. Next add Solution 3
until the tube is half full, cork it and shake it a bit. A second
tube is filled a quarter full with dry, fine soil from the sample.
The contents of the first tube are then added to the soil sample, the mixture is corked and shaken strongly for no less than
thirty seconds. Place a filter paper in one of the funnels provided with the kit and filter the solution back into tube num-

ber one. When the solution drips through, compare the colors of the filtrate with the colors on the chart. Here, the darker the color of the filtered solution, the better off you are, as a pale yellow or near colorless solution means you have almost a 10 percent nitrogen deficiency, while a deep brown means the deficiency is 2 percent or less.

Phosphorus Deficiency Testing

Another clean test tube is needed. This is filled an eighth full of Solution 4, then brought up to half with Solution 5, and given a mild shake. A second tube is filled a quarter full of the soil sample, and the contents of the first tube are then added and shaken well for thirty seconds or so. This result is now filtered, as was the nitrogen test solution, using a clean filter paper and funnel, back into the first test tube. Once the clear or mildly tinted filtrate drips through, you take the tin rod, scrape it gently with a sharp knife, and use the rod to stir the extract. The solution will slowly turn blue, which is then compared for shade intensity to the chart supplied. Again, the darker the better. If you don't get any color after stirring with the rod, drop in just a tiny amount of Solution 4 and restir. Incidentally, the chemicals in this test may cause some highly alkaline soils to effervesce a fair amount when they are mixed with the solution. Let the solution drip in on the soil sample very slowly so that it doesn't bubble right on out of the test tube.

Potassium Testing

Fill a clean test tube a quarter full of Solution 6, bringing the total to half full with Solution 7. Shake lightly. Take a second tube, again a quarter full of the soil sample, and add the contents of the first tube to that. Shake for half a minute, strongly. Filter the solution back into the first tube and make the usual color comparison.

While all of this may sound time consuming, it is not. Once you are set up, have the dry soil sample, and have opened up the kit's case, things actually go quite rapidly. (Some of the solutions to be filtered can take a long time to drip through — in one case I waited nearly half an hour because I couldn't locate, out in the field, a clean utensil to sort of help things along a bit — but you can almost always go on to the start of another test when this happens, so that progress is steady.) Make notes of the proportions of fertilizers that are needed in particular areas. In most cases we will do well to remember that it is definitely possible to overfertilize: for example, too much potassium will make plants susceptible to holding too much water, and that makes them, in turn, liable to injury from frost when frost might otherwise not be serious enough to cause injury. Still, the correct amount is essential to hardiness in root, tuberous, and bulb plants of all kinds. Excess nitrogen can also cause difficulty through overrapid growth, resulting in overall tissue softness and weak plants; adequate nitrogen gives you a strong, healthy plant with strong stalks and active vegetative growth. In fact, nitrogen acts so strongly on vegetative growth that overfeeding a plant nitrogen during its flowering time will stop the flowering and cause vegetative growth to restart. And depending on the amount of overfeeding, this can result in a great deal of retardation in flower and seed formation.

Once the soil type and soil condition are known, you are ready to go on to the care and feeding of your soil, to preparing it to produce the plants you wish to have. (Fig. 3-2)

pH PREFERENCE of FLOWERS, HOUSE PLANTS, ORNAMENTALS and LAWN GRASSES

Plant	pH	Plant	pH	Plant	pH
Abutilon	5.5-6.5	Crab, Flowering	5.0-6.5	Heather	4.5-6.0
Acacia	6.0-8.0	Crassula	5.0-6.0	Heliotrope	6.0-8.0
Aechmea	5.0-5.5	Creeping Fig	5.0-6.0	Helxine	5.0-6.0
African Daisy	6.0-7.5	Crocus	6.0-8.0	Hemlock	5.0-6.0
African Violet	5.5-7.5	Croton	5.0-6.0	Hens-and-Chickens	6.0-8.0
Ageratum, Blue	6.0-7.5	Crown-of-Thorns	6.0-7.5	Hibiscus, Chinese	6.0-8.0
Aglaonema	5.0-6.0	Cyclamen	6.0-7.0	Holly, English	4.0-5.5
Almond	6.0-7.0	Daffodil	6.0-6.5	American	5.0-6.0
Alyssum	6.0-7.5	Dahlia	6.0-7.5	Hollyhock	6.0-8.0
Amaryllis	5.5-6.5	Daisy, Ox-Eye (wild)	6.0-7.5	Honeysuckle Bush	6.5-8.0
Anemone	5.0-6.5	Daisy, Shasta	5.0-6.0	Hoya	5.0-6.5
Anthurium	5.0-6.0	Daphne	6.5-7.5	Hyacinth	6.5-7.5
Araucaria	5.0-6.0	Delphinium	6.0-7.5	Hydrangea, Blue	4.0-5.0
Arbor Vitae	6.0-7.5	Deutzia	6.0-7.5	Pink	6.0-7.0
Arbutus, Trailing	4.0-5.0	Didiscus	6.0-7.0	White	6.0-8.0
Aspidistra	4.0-5.5	Dieffenbachia	5.0-6.0	Impatiens	5.5-6.5
Aster	6.5-7.0	Dogwood	5.0-6.0	Indian Pipe	5.0-6.0
Azalea	4.5-6.0	Dracaena	5.0-6.0	Iresine	5.0-6.5
Baby's Breath		Episcia	6.0-7.0	Iris	5.5-7.5
(Gypsophila)	6.0-7.5	Eucalyptus	6.0-8.0	Iris, Japanese	5.5-6.5
Baby's Tears	5.0-5.5	Euphorbia	6.0-7.0	Ivy: Boston	6.0-8.0
Bachelor Button	6.0-7.5	Ferns: Asparagus	6.0-8.0	English	6.0-8.0
Barberry	6.0-7.5	Bird's Nest	5.0-5.5	Grape	5.0-6.5
Bayberry	5.0-6.0	Boston	5.5-6.5	Jack-in-Pulpit	6.0-8.0
Begonia	5.5-7.0	Maidenhair	6.0-8.0	Jacob's Ladder	5.0-7.5
Billbergia	5.0-6.0	Feverfew	6.5-7.0	Jasmine	5.5-7.0
Bird-of-Paradise	6.0-6.5	Fir: Balsam	5.0-6.0	Jerusalem Cherry	5.5-6.5
Bleeding-Heart	6.0-7.5	Douglas	6.0-7.0	Lady's Slipper	5.0-6.0
Bloodleaf	5.5-6.5	Fittonia	5.5-6.5	Lady's Slipper, Showy	6.0-8.0
Blue Bell	6.0-7.5	Forget-Me-Not	6.0-8.0	Larkspur	6.0-7.5
Bougainvillea	5.5-7.5	Forsythia	6.0-8.0	Laurel	4.5-6.0
Bouvardia	5.5-6.5	Foxglove	6.0-7.5	Lemon Plant	6.0-7.5
Boxwood	6.0-7.5	Freesia	6.0-7.5	Lilac	6.0-7.5
Bridal Wreath	6.0-8.0	Fuchsia	5.5-6.5	Lily: Calla	6.0-7.0
Burning Bush	5.5-7.5	Gardenia	5.0-6.0	Day	6.0-8.0
Butterfly Bush	6.0-7.5	Genista	6.5-7.5	Easter	6.0-7.0
Cacti	4.5-6.0	Geranium	6.0-8.0	Madonna	6.5-7.5
Cactus, Christmas	5.0-6.5	Gerbera	6.0-7.0	Tiger	6.0-7.0
Calendula	5.5-7.0	Gladiolus	6.0-7.0	-of-the-Valley	4.5-6.0
Camellia	4.5-5.5	Gloxinia	5.5-6.5	Lupine	5.0-6.0
Campanula	5.5-6.5	Godetia	6.0-7.5	Magnolia, Sweet Bay	4.0-5.0
Candytuft	5.5-7.0	Grass: Bent	5.5-6.5	Maple, Japanese	6.0-8.0
Canna	6.0-8.0	Bermuda	5.0-7.0	Maranta	5.0-6.0
Carnation	6.0-7.5	Blue, Kentucky	6.0-7.5	Marigold	5.5-7.0
Chrysanthemum	6.0-7.5	Buffalo	6.0-8.5	Mignonette	5.0-8.0
Cineraria	5.5-7.0	Carpet	4.5-7.0	Mock Orange	6.0-8.0
Cissus	5.0-6.0	Centipede	4.0-6.0	Monstera	5.0-6.0
Clarkia	6.0-6.5	Clover	5.5-7.0	Morning Glory	6.0-7.5
Clematis	5.5-7.0	Fescue	5.5-7.5	Myrtle	6.0-8.0
Clerodendren	5.0-6.0	Grama	6.0-8.5	Narcissus	6.0-7.0
Clivia	5.5-6.5	Red Top	5.0-7.5	Nasturtium	5.5-7.5
Coleus	6.0-7.0	Ryegrass	5.5-8.0	Neomarica	5.5-6.5
Columbine	5.5-7.0	St. Augustine	6.0-8.0	Nephthytis	4.5-5.5
Columnea	4.5-5.5	Wheatgrass	6.0-8.5	Oleander	6.0-7.5
Coral Bells	6.0-7.0	Zoysia	4.5-7.5	Orange Plant	6.0-7.5
Coreopsis Trefoil	5.0-6.0	Grevillea	5.5-6.5	Orchid	4.5-5.5
Cosmos	5.0-8.0	Gynura	5.5-6.5	Osage Orange	6.0-7.5
Coxcomb	6.0-7.5	Hawthorne	6.0-7.0	Oxalis	6.0-8.0

Fig. 3-2

Plant	pH	Plant	pH	Plant	pH
Palm, Cocos	6.0-7.5	Primrose	5.5-6.5	Stock	6.0-7.5
Pandanus	5.0-6.0	Pyrethrum	6.0-7.5	Sunflower	6.0-7.5
Pansy	5.5-6.5	Quince,		Swainsonia	6.0-7.0
Passion Vine	6.0-7.0	Japanese flowering	6.0-7.0	Sweet Pea	6.0-7.5
Peony	6.0-7.5	Red Hot Poker	6.0-7.5	Sweet William	6.0-7.5
Peperomia	5.0-6.0	Rhododendron	4.5-6.0	Tradescantia	5.0-6.0
Petunia	6.0-7.5	Rose	6.0-7.0	Tuberose	6.0-7.0
Philodendron	5.0-6.0	Rose of Sharon (Althea)	6.0-7.5	Tulip	6.0-7.0
Phlox	5.0-6.0	Rubber Plant	5.0-6.0	Verbena	6.0-8.0
Pick-a-Back Plant		St. Paulia	6.0-7.0	Violet, Common	5.0-7.5
(Tolmeia)	5.0-6.0	Salvia	6.0-7.5	Dogtooth	5.0-6.0
Pine, White	4.5-6.0	Sansevieria	4.5-7.0	Water Lily	5.5-6.5
Pink	6.0-8.0	Scabiosa	5.0-7.5	Wisteria	6.0-8.0
Pitcherplant	4.0-5.5	Scilla	6.0-8.0	Woodbine	6.0-7.0
Plumbago	5.5-6.5	Shrimp Plant	5.5-6.5	Yew, Japanese	6.0-7.0
Pogonia, Rose	4.0-5.0	Snapdragon	6.0-7.5	Yucca	6.0-8.0
Poinsettia	6.0-7.5	Snowdrop	6.0-8.0	Zebrina	5.0-6.0
Poppy	6.0-7.5	Spirea	6.0-7.5	Zinnia	5.5-7.5
Portulaca	5.5-7.5	Spruce, Colorado	6.0-7.0		
Pothos	5.0-6.0	Star of Bethlehem	6.0-8.0		

pH PREFERENCE of VEGETABLES, FRUIT TREES, and FIELD CROPS

Crop	pH	Crop	pH	Crop	pH
Alfalfa	6.0-8.0	Currants, Red	5.5-7.0	Peppers	5.5-7.0
Apples	5.0-6.5	Eggplant	5.5-6.5	Pineapple	5.0-6.0
Artichoke (Jerusalem)	6.5-7.5	Endive	5.8-7.0	Plums, American	6.0-8.0
Asparagus	6.0-8.0	Garlic	5.5-8.0	Potatoes	4.8-6.5
Avocado	6.0-8.0	Gooseberries	5.0-6.5	Sweet Potatoes	5.2-6.0
Banana	5.0-7.0	Grapes	5.5-7.0	Pumpkin	5.5-7.5
Barley	6.5-7.8	Grapefruit	6.0-7.5	Quince	6.0-7.5
Beans: Lima	6.0-7.0	Hazel Nuts	6.0-7.0	Radishes	6.0-7.0
Pole	6.0-7.5	Hickory Nuts	6.0-7.0	Raspberries, Black	5.0-6.5
Beets, Sugar	6.5-8.0	Horseradishes	6.0-7.0	Red	5.5-7.0
Table	6.0-7.5	Kale	6.0-7.5	Rhubarb	5.5-7.0
Blackberries	5.0-6.0	Kentucky Coffee	6.0-8.0	Rutabaga	5.5-7.0
Blueberries	4.0-5.5	Kohl-Rabi	6.0-7.5	Rye	5.0-7.0
Broccoli	6.0-7.0	Kumquats	5.5-6.5	Sage	5.5-6.5
Broom Sedge	4.5-6.0	Leek	6.0-8.0	Salsify	6.0-7.5
Brussels Sprouts	6.0-7.5	Lemon	6.0-7.0	Shallot	5.5-7.0
Buckwheat	5.5-7.0	Lentil	5.5-7.0	Sorghum	5.5-7.5
Cabbage	6.0-7.5	Lespedeza	4.5-6.5	Soybeans	6.0-7.0
Cantaloupe (Muskmelon)	6.0-7.5	Lettuce	6.0-7.0	Spinach	6.0-7.5
Carrots	5.5-7.0	Millet	5.0-6.5	Squash, Crookneck	6.0-7.5
Cashew	5.0-6.0	Mushrooms	6.5-7.5	Hubbard	5.5-7.0
Cauliflower	5.5-7.5	Mustard	6.0-7.5	Strawberries	5.0-6.5
Celery	5.8-7.0	Oats	5.0-7.5	Swiss Chard	6.0-7.5
Cherry (Sweet)	6.0-7.5	Okra	6.0-7.5	Thyme	5.5-7.0
(Sour)	6.0-7.0	Olives	5.5-6.5	Timothy	5.5-6.5
Chicory	5.0-6.5	Onions	6.0-7.0	Tobacco	
Chives	6.0-7.0	Oranges	6.0-7.5	(according to species)	5.5-7.5
Clover, Red	6.0-7.5	Parsley	5.0-7.0	Tomatoes	5.5-7.5
Corn	5.5-7.5	Parsnip	5.5-7.0	Turnips	5.5-6.8
Cotton, Upland	5.0-6.0	Peas	6.0-7.5	Vetch	5.2-7.0
Cowpeas	5.0-6.5	Peach	6.0-7.5	Walnuts	6.0-8.0
Crabapples	6.0-7.5	Peanuts	5.3-6.6	Watercress	6.0-8.0
Cranberries	4.2-5.0	Pears	6.0-7.5	Watermelon	5.5-6.5
Cucumbers	5.5-7.0	Pecans	6.4-8.0	Wheat	5.5-7.5

Fig. 3-2

Chapter 4

SOIL CARE

Soil care starts at different times of the year. For those who
are putting in new gardens and find themselves able to do so
in the fall, luck is good. For fall soil preparation means they'll
be ready to go, come spring, with very little preparation beyond
checking soil temperature to make sure the seeds will sprout
after being planted. In fact, if the soil is already fertilized and
ready to go, soil temperature tests are the first to be made in
a spring flower garden. If soil temperature is low, bacteria and
other microorganisms won't be working, and seed germination
cannot take place. It makes no sense at all to start planting
before soil temperature reaches about 55°F., and many plants,
whether planted as seed or seedling, need higher temperatures.
Generally, recommendations for such plants as tomatoes and
peppers say they should not be planted until night *air* temperatures reach and maintain 50°F. or higher. Well, night soil
temperatures should be considerably warmer than air temperatures even a few inches below the surface. If they're not, your
transplants are not going to do well. At best, they will be
stunted; at worst, they will die without ever really taking hold.
Mulching can help to increase soil temperatures to the point
where bacteria are consistently active a bit earlier in the year;
but a garden mulched through the winter may actually take a

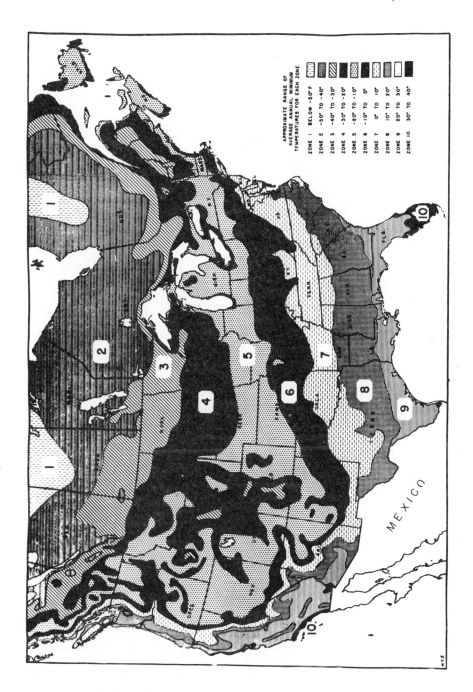

Fig. 4-1. Plant Hardiness Map

bit longer to warm up to the correct temperature, since the
mulch insulates the ground from heat as well as from cold.

Soil temperature also affects the rate at which the roots of
plants absorb water from the soil. Absorption slows greatly
as the soil temperature drops. For this reason, the person who
waters the garden on a summer day with normal tap water —
say, in the 55° F. range — may be surprised that the heat-
wilted plants do not immediately recover. In fact, because
the cold water may drop the soil temperature considerably,
the plants can wilt even more, the roots becoming even less
able to absorb water. (Fig. 4-1)

Transpiration, the giving off of water by plant leaves, can,
on a hot day and in a sandy soil, be greater than the intake of
water by the roots. This is the cause of most wilting under
such conditions. If watering to correct wilt is to be done, then
either one of two methods should be followed. The best (and
easiest) is to water plants in the evening, when soil and water
temperatures are a great deal closer together. Next best is to
use only water that has been warmed by the sun or by some
other means. Keeping full watering cans located around a
large flower or vegetable garden during the day is more than
a slight problem; for smaller gardens, the idea works fine. Over
the years I have helped water gardens from cans and jugs when
the gardens were distant from a decent water supply, but in no
way is such a job one of the pleasures of gardening. (Figs. 4-2,
4-3, 4-4)

Balancing pH

Many substances can be used to cut the acidity of garden soils,
but all contain some form of lime, so that the soil not only is
sweetened, but also receives the calcium necessary for good
plant growth. Dolomitic limes will provide magnesium as well
in amounts sufficient for healthy plant growth. The chemical

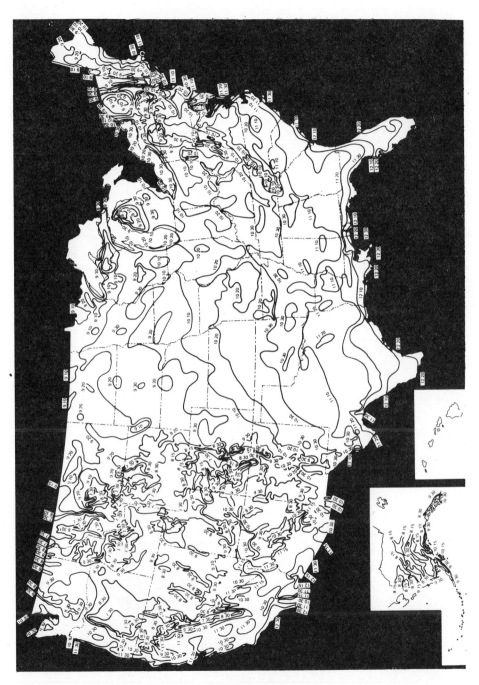

Fig. 4-2. Average Dates of the First Killing Frost in Fall

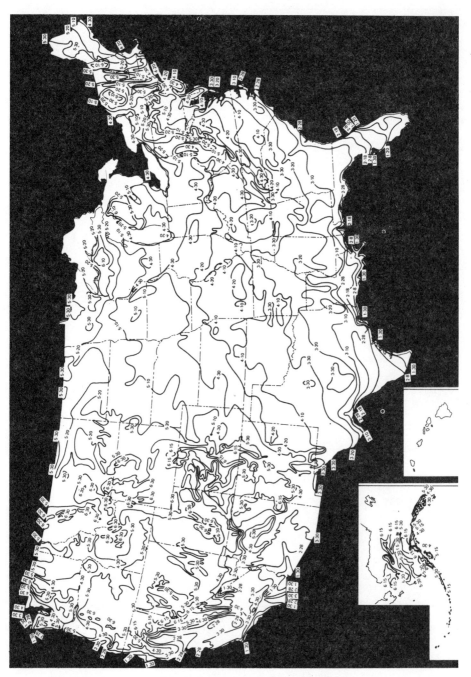

Fig. 4-3. Average Dates of the Last Killing Frost in Spring

formula for lime (or quicklime) is CaO, and it is derived from limestones, chalk, and marble — the calcium carbonates ($CaCO_3$) — by heating them. This produces CaO while releasing carbon dioxide. By combining the CaO with water, hydrate of lime is formed. Hydrate of lime — $Ca(OH)_2$ — is also called slaked lime.

Quicklime is highly reactive with water. Thus it can only be used in very well watered soils; otherwise it will tear the water from the soil organisms and form hydrated lime, thus burning the soil and killing the plants. In soils that have been nitrogen fertilized, CaO combines with the nitrogen compounds to release gaseous nitrogen, thereby robbing the soil of needed nutrients. Thus quicklime is seldom recommended as the way to sweeten soils.

Hydrate of lime will not burn plants, but because of its easily soluble form, leaching is a problem in areas of heavy rainfall. Because we would wish a liming to last for more than a single season — in some cases, hydrate of lime would not even last *through* a single growing season — hydrate of lime is seldom the substance to use to change pH.

Lime in soil serves several functions in addition to swinging the pH balance away from acidity. Some of the potash and phosphorus are changed from insoluble compounds to soluble types useful to your plants, while the lime also tends to cause clay soils to clump in larger particles, thereby aiding the penetration by air and water. Oddly enough, though lime tends to open up clayey soils, it serves just the opposite purpose with sandy soils. Soil particles are held more closely clumped, and that aids water retention.

Many compounds other than limestone can be used to put lime into the soil. Chalk, dolomite, gypsum, oyster shells, and wood ashes are all good sources, as is bonemeal.

Crop	Jan. 30	Feb. 8	Feb. 18
Asparagus [1]			
Beans, lima	Feb. 1–Apr. 15	Feb. 10–May 1	Mar. 1–May 1
Beans, snap	Feb. 1–Apr. 1	Feb. 1–May 1	Mar. 1–May 1
Beet	Jan. 1–Mar. 15	Jan. 10–Mar. 15	Jan. 20–Apr. 1
Broccoli, sprouting [1]	Jan. 1–30	Jan. 1–30	Jan. 15–Feb. 15
Brussels sprouts [1]	Jan. 1–30	Jan. 1–30	Jan. 15–Feb. 15
Cabbage [1]	Jan. 1–15	Jan. 1–Feb. 10	Jan. 1–Feb. 25
Cabbage, Chinese	([2])	([2])	([2])
Carrot	Jan. 1–Mar. 1	Jan. 1–Mar. 1	Jan. 15–Mar. 1
Cauliflower [1]	Jan. 1–Feb. 1	Jan. 1–Feb. 1	Jan. 10–Feb. 10
Celery and celeriac	Jan. 1–Feb. 1	Jan. 10–Feb. 10	Jan. 20–Feb. 20
Chard	Jan. 1–Apr. 1	Jan. 10–Apr. 1	Jan. 20–Apr. 15
Chervil and chives	Jan. 1–Feb. 1	Jan. 1–Feb. 1	Jan. 1–Feb. 1
Chicory, witloof			
Collards [1]	Jan. 1–Feb. 15	Jan. 1–Feb. 15	Jan. 1–Mar. 15
Cornsalad	Jan. 1–Feb. 15	Jan. 1–Feb. 15	Jan. 1–Mar. 15
Corn, sweet	Feb. 1–Mar. 15	Feb. 10–Apr. 1	Feb. 20–Apr. 15
Cress, upland	Jan. 1–Feb. 1	Jan. 1–Feb. 15	Jan. 15–Feb. 15
Cucumber	Feb. 15–Mar. 15	Feb. 15–Apr. 1	Feb. 15–Apr. 15
Eggplant [1]	Feb. 1–Mar. 1	Feb. 10–Mar. 15	Feb. 20–Apr. 1
Endive	Jan. 1–Mar. 1	Jan. 1–Mar. 1	Jan. 15–Mar. 1
Fennel, Florence	Jan. 1–Mar. 1	Jan. 1–Mar. 1	Jan. 15–Mar. 1
Garlic	([2])	([2])	([2])
Horseradish [1]			
Kale	Jan. 1–Feb. 1	Jan. 10–Feb. 1	Jan. 20–Feb. 10
Kohlrabi	Jan. 1–Feb. 1	Jan. 10–Feb. 1	Jan. 20–Feb. 10
Leek	Jan. 1–Feb. 1	Jan. 1–Feb. 1	Jan. 1–Feb. 15
Lettuce, head [1]	Jan. 1–Feb. 1	Jan. 1–Feb. 1	Jan. 1–Feb. 1
Lettuce, leaf	Jan. 1–Feb. 1	Jan. 1–Feb. 1	Jan. 1–Mar. 15
Muskmelon	Feb. 15–Mar. 15	Feb. 15–Apr. 1	Feb. 15–Apr. 15
Mustard	Jan. 1–Mar. 1	Jan. 1–Mar. 1	Feb. 15–Apr. 15
Okra	Feb. 15–Apr. 1	Feb. 15–Apr. 15	Mar. 1–June 1
Onion [1]	Jan. 1–15	Jan. 1–15	Jan. 1–15
Onion, seed	Jan. 1–15	Jan. 1–15	Jan. 1–15
Onion, sets	Jan. 1–15	Jan. 1–15	Jan. 1–15
Parsley	Jan. 1–30	Jan. 1–30	Jan. 1–30
Parsnip			Jan. 1–Feb. 1
Peas, garden	Jan. 1–Feb. 15	Jan. 1–Feb. 15	Jan. 1–Mar. 1
Peas, black-eye	Feb. 15–May 1	Feb. 15–May 15	Mar. 1–June 15
Pepper [1]	Feb. 1–Apr. 1	Feb. 15–Apr. 15	Mar. 1–May 1
Potato	Jan. 1–Feb. 15	Jan. 1–Feb. 15	Jan. 15–Mar. 1
Radish	Jan. 1–Apr. 1	Jan. 1–Apr. 1	Jan. 1–Apr. 1
Rhubarb [1]			
Rutabaga			
Salsify	Jan. 1–Feb. 1	Jan. 10–Feb. 10	Jan. 15–Feb. 20
Shallot	Jan. 1–Feb. 1	Jan. 1–Feb. 10	Jan. 15–Feb. 20
Sorrel	Jan. 1–Mar. 1	Jan. 1–Mar. 1	Jan. 15–Mar. 1
Soybean	Mar. 1–June 30	Mar. 1–June 30	Mar. 10–June 30
Spinach	Jan. 1–Feb. 15	Jan. 1–Feb. 15	Jan. 1–Mar. 1
Spinach, New Zealand	Feb. 1–Apr. 15	Feb. 1–Apr. 15	Mar. 1–Apr. 15
Squash, summer	Feb. 1–Apr. 15	Feb. 15–Apr. 15	Mar. 1–Apr. 15
Sweetpotato	Feb. 15–May 15	Mar. 1–May 15	Mar. 20–June 1
Tomato	Feb. 1–Apr. 1	Feb. 20–Apr. 10	Mar. 1–Apr. 20
Turnip	Jan. 1–Mar. 1	Jan. 1–Mar. 1	Jan. 10–Mar. 1
Watermelon	Feb. 15–Mar. 15	Feb. 15–Apr. 1	Feb. 15–Apr. 15

[1] Plants.
[2] Generally fall-planted (table 5).

Fig. 4-4. Earliest Dates and Range of Dates for Safe Spring Planting of Vegetables in the Open

Feb. 28	Mar. 10	Mar. 20	Mar. 30
	Jan. 1–Mar. 1	Feb. 1–Mar. 10	Feb. 15–Mar. 20.
Mar. 15–June 1	Mar. 20–June 1	Apr. 1–June 15	Apr. 15–June 20.
Mar. 10–May 15	Mar. 15–May 15	Mar. 15–May 25	Apr. 1–June 1.
Feb. 1–Apr. 15	Feb. 15–June 1	Feb. 15–May 15	Mar. 1–June 1.
Feb. 1–Mar. 1	Feb. 15–Mar. 15	Feb. 15–Mar. 15	Mar. 1–20.
Feb. 1–Mar. 1	Feb. 15–Mar. 15	Feb. 15–Mar. 15	Mar. 1–20.
Jan. 15–Feb. 25	Jan. 25–Mar. 1	Feb. 1–Mar. 1	Feb. 15–Mar. 10.
(2)	(2)	(2)	(2)
Feb. 1–Mar. 1	Feb. 10–Mar. 15	Feb. 15–Mar. 20	Mar. 1–Apr. 10.
Jan. 20–Feb. 20	Feb. 1–Mar. 1	Feb. 10–Mar. 10	Feb. 20–Mar. 20.
Feb. 1–Mar. 1	Feb. 20–Mar. 20	Mar. 1–Apr. 1	Mar. 15–Apr. 15.
Feb. 1–May 1	Feb. 15–May 15	Feb. 20–May 15	Mar. 1–May 25.
Jan. 15–Feb. 15	Feb. 1–Mar. 1	Feb. 10–Mar. 10	Feb. 15–Mar. 15.
	June 1–July 1	June 1–July 1	June 1–July 1.
Jan. 15–Mar. 15	Feb. 1–Apr. 1	Feb. 15–May 1	Mar. 1–June 1.
Jan. 1–Mar. 1	Jan. 1–Mar. 15	Jan. 1–Mar. 15	Jan. 15–Mar. 15.
Mar. 1–Apr. 15	Mar. 10–Apr. 15	Mar. 15–May 1	Mar. 25–May 15.
Feb. 1–Mar. 1	Feb. 10–Mar. 15	Feb. 20–Mar. 15	Mar. 1–Apr. 1.
Mar. 1–Apr. 15	Mar. 15–Apr. 15	Apr. 1–May 1	Apr. 10–May 15.
Mar. 10–Apr. 15	Mar. 15–Apr. 15	Apr. 1–May 1	Apr. 15–May 15.
Feb. 1–Mar. 1	Feb. 15–Mar. 15	Mar. 1–Apr. 1	Mar. 10–Apr. 10.
Feb. 1–Mar. 1	Feb. 15–Mar. 15	Mar. 1–Apr. 1	Mar. 10–Apr. 10.
(2)	(2)	Feb. 1–Mar. 1	Feb. 10–Mar. 10.
			Mar. 1–Apr. 1.
Feb. 1–20	Feb. 10–Mar. 1	Feb. 20–Mar. 10	Mar. 1–20.
Feb. 1–20	Feb. 10–Mar. 1	Feb. 20–Mar. 10	Mar. 1–Apr. 1.
Jan. 15–Feb. 15	Jan. 25–Mar. 1	Feb. 1–Mar. 1	Feb. 15–Mar. 15.
Jan. 15–Feb. 15	Feb. 1–20	Feb. 15–Mar. 10	Mar. 1–20.
Jan. 1–Mar. 15	Jan. 15–Apr. 1	Feb. 1–Apr. 1	Feb. 15–Apr. 15.
Mar. 1–Apr. 15	Mar. 15–Apr. 15	Apr. 1–May 1	Apr. 10–May 15.
Feb. 1–Mar. 1	Feb. 10–Mar. 15	Feb. 20–Apr. 1	Mar. 1–Apr. 15.
Mar. 10–June 1	Mar. 20–June 1	Apr. 1–June 15	Apr. 10–June 15.
Jan. 1–Feb. 1	Jan. 15–Feb. 15	Feb. 10–Mar. 10	Feb. 15–Mar. 15.
Jan. 1–Feb. 15	Feb. 1–Mar. 1	Feb. 10–Mar. 10	Feb. 20–Mar. 15.
Jan. 1–Mar. 1	Jan. 15–Mar. 10	Feb. 1–Mar. 20	Feb. 15–Mar. 20.
Jan. 15–Mar. 1	Feb. 1–Mar. 10	Feb. 15–Mar. 15	Mar. 1–Apr. 1.
Jan. 15–Feb. 15	Jan. 15–Mar. 1	Feb. 15–Mar. 15	Mar. 1–Apr. 1.
Jan. 15–Mar. 1	Jan. 15–Mar. 15	Feb. 1–Mar. 15	Feb. 10–Mar. 20.
Mar. 10–June 20	Mar. 15–July 1	Apr. 1–July 1	Apr. 15–July 1.
Mar. 15–May 1	Apr. 1–June 1	Apr. 10–June 1	Apr. 15–June 1.
Jan. 15–Mar. 1	Feb. 1–Mar. 1	Feb. 10–Mar. 15	Feb. 20–Mar. 20.
Jan. 1–Apr. 1	Jan. 1–Apr. 15	Jan. 20–May 1	Feb. 15–May 1.
Jan. 1–Feb. 1	Jan. 15–Feb. 15	Jan. 15–Mar. 1	Feb. 1–Mar. 1.
Jan. 15–Mar. 1	Feb. 1–Mar. 1	Feb. 15–Mar. 1	Mar. 1–15.
Jan. 1–Mar. 1	Jan. 15–Mar. 1	Feb. 1–Mar. 10	Feb. 15–Mar. 15.
Feb. 1–Mar. 10	Feb. 10–Mar. 15	Feb. 10–Mar. 20	Feb. 20–Apr. 1.
Mar. 20–June 30	Apr. 10–June 30	Apr. 10–June 30	Apr. 20–June 30.
Jan. 1–Mar. 1	Jan. 15–Mar. 10	Jan. 15–Mar. 15	Feb. 1–Mar. 20.
Mar. 15–May 15	Mar. 20–May 15	Apr. 1–May 15	Apr. 10–June 1.
Mar. 15–May 15	Mar. 15–May 1	Apr. 1–May 15	Apr. 10–June 1.
Mar. 20–June 1	Apr. 1–June 1	Apr. 10–June 1	Apr. 20–June 1.
Mar. 10–May 1	Mar. 20–May 10	Apr. 1–May 20	Apr. 10–June 1.
Jan. 20–Mar. 1	Feb. 1–Mar. 1	Feb. 10–Mar. 10	Feb. 20–Mar. 20.
Mar. 1–Apr. 15	Mar. 15–Apr. 15	Apr. 1–May 1	Apr. 10–May 15.

Crop	Apr. 10	Apr. 20	Apr. 30
Asparagus [1]	Mar. 10–Apr. 10	Mar. 15–Apr. 15	Mar. 20–Apr. 15
Beans, lima	Apr. 1–June 30	May 1–June 20	May 15–June 15
Beans, snap	Apr. 10–June 30	Apr. 25–June 30	May 10–June 30
Beet	Mar. 10–June 1	Mar. 20–June 1	Apr. 1–June 15
Broccoli, sprouting [1]	Mar. 15–Apr. 15	Mar. 25–Apr. 20	Apr. 1–May 1
Brussels sprouts [1]	Mar. 15–Apr. 15	Mar. 25–Apr. 20	Apr. 1–May 1
Cabbage [1]	Mar. 1–Apr. 1	Mar. 10–Apr. 1	Mar. 15–Apr. 10
Cabbage, Chinese	(2)	(2)	(2)
Carrot	Mar. 10–Apr. 20	Apr. 1–May 15	Apr. 10–June 1
Cauliflower [1]	Mar. 1–Mar. 20	Mar. 15–Apr. 20	Apr. 10–May 10
Celery and celeriac	Apr. 1–Apr. 20	Apr. 10–May 1	Apr. 15–May 1
Chard	Mar. 15–June 15	Apr. 1–June 15	Apr. 15–June 15
Chervil and chives	Mar. 1–Apr. 1	Mar. 10–Apr. 10	Mar. 20–Apr. 20
Chicory, witloof	June 10–July 1	June 15–July 1	June 15–July 1
Collards [1]	Mar. 1–June 1	Mar. 10–June 1	Apr. 1–June 1
Cornsalad	Feb. 1–Apr. 1	Feb. 15–Apr. 15	Mar. 1–May 1
Corn, sweet	Apr. 10–June 1	Apr. 25–June 15	May 10–June 15
Cress, upland	Mar. 10–Apr. 15	Mar. 20–May 1	Apr. 10–May 10
Cucumber	Apr. 20–June 1	May 1–June 15	May 15–June 15
Eggplant [1]	May 1–June 1	May 10–June 1	May 15–June 10
Endive	Mar. 15–Apr. 15	Mar. 25–Apr. 15	Apr. 1–May 1
Fennel, Florence	Mar. 15–Apr. 15	Mar. 25–Apr. 15	Apr. 1–May 1
Garlic	Feb. 20–Mar. 20	Mar. 10–Apr. 1	Mar. 15–Apr. 15
Horseradish [1]	Mar. 10–Apr. 10	Mar. 20–Apr. 20	Apr. 1–30
Kale	Mar. 10–Apr. 1	Mar. 20–Apr. 10	Apr. 1–20
Kohlrabi	Mar. 10–Apr. 10	Mar. 20–May 1	Apr. 1–May 10
Leek	Mar. 1–Apr. 1	Mar. 15–Apr. 15	Apr. 1–May 1
Lettuce, head [1]	Mar. 10–Apr. 1	Mar. 20–Apr. 15	Apr. 1–May 1
Lettuce, leaf	Mar. 15–May 15	Mar. 20–May 15	Apr. 1–June 1
Muskmelon	Apr. 20–June 1	May 1–June 15	May 15–June 15
Mustard	Mar. 10–Apr. 20	Mar. 20–May 1	Apr. 1–May 10
Okra	Apr. 20–June 15	May 1–June 1	May 10–June 1
Onion [1]	Mar. 1–Apr. 1	Mar. 15–Apr. 10	Apr. 1–May 1
Onion, seed	Mar. 1–Apr. 1	Mar. 15–Apr. 1	Mar. 15–Apr. 15
Onion, sets	Mar. 1–Apr. 1	Mar. 10–Apr. 1	Mar. 10–Apr. 10
Parsley	Mar. 10–Apr. 10	Mar. 20–Apr. 20	Apr. 1–May 1
Parsnip	Mar. 10–Apr. 10	Mar. 20–Apr. 20	Apr. 1–May 1
Peas, garden	Feb. 20–Mar. 20	Mar. 10–Apr. 10	Mar. 20–May 1
Peas, black-eye	May 1–July 1	May 10–June 15	May 15–June 1
Pepper [1]	May 1–June 1	May 10–June 1	May 15–June 10
Potato	Mar. 10–Apr. 1	Mar. 15–Apr. 10	Mar. 20–May 10
Radish	Mar. 1–May 1	Mar. 10–May 10	Mar. 20–May 10
Rhubarb [1]	Mar. 1–Apr. 1	Mar. 10–Apr. 10	Mar. 20–Apr. 15
Rutabaga			May 1–June 1
Salsify	Mar. 10–Apr. 15	Mar. 20–May 1	Apr. 1–May 15
Shallot	Mar. 1–Apr. 1	Mar. 15–Apr. 15	Apr. 1–May 1
Sorrel	Mar. 1–Apr. 15	Mar. 15–May 1	Apr. 1–May 15
Soybean	May 1–June 30	May 10–June 20	May 15–June 15
Spinach	Feb. 15–Apr. 1	Mar. 1–Apr. 15	Mar. 20–Apr. 20
Spinach, New Zealand	Apr. 20–June 1	May 1–June 15	May 1–June 15
Squash, summer	Apr. 20–June 1	May 1–June 15	May 1–30
Sweetpotato	May 1–June 1	May 10–June 10	May 20–June 10
Tomato	Apr. 20–June 1	May 5–June 10	May 10–June 15
Turnip	Mar. 1–Apr. 1	Mar. 10–Apr. 1	Mar. 20–May 1
Watermelon	Apr. 20–June 1	May 1–June 15	May 15–June 15

[1] Plants.
[2] Generally fall-planted (table 5).

May 10	May 20	May 30	June 10
Mar. 10–Apr. 30 ----	Apr. 20–May 15 ----	May 1–June 1 ----	May 15–June 1.
May 25–June 15 ---			
May 10–June 30 ---	May–15–June 30 ---	May 25–June 15 ---	
Apr. 15–June 15 ---	Apr. 25–June 15 ---	May 1–June 15 ----	May 15–June 15.
Apr. 15–June 1 ----	May 1–June 15 ----	May 10–June 10 ---	May 20–June 10.
Apr. 15–June 1 ----	May 1–June 15 ----	May 10–June 10 ---	May 20–June 10.
Apr. 1–May 15 -----	May 1–June 15 ----	May 10–June 15 ---	May 20–June 1.
Apr. 1–May 15 -----	May 1–June 15 ----	May 10–June 15 ---	May 20–June 1.
Apr. 20–June 15 ---	May 1–June 1 ----	May 10–June 1 ----	May 20–June 1.
Apr. 15–May 15 ----	May 10–June 15 ---	May 20–June 1 ----	June 1- June 15.
Apr. 20–June 15 ---	May 10–June 15 ---	May 20–June 1 ----	June 1–June 15.
Apr. 20–June 15 ---	May 10–June 15 ---	May 20–June 1 ----	June 1–June 15.
Apr. 1–May 1 ------	Apr. 15–May 15 ----	May 1–June 1 -----	May 15–June 1.
June 1–20 ---------	June 1–15 ----------	June 1–15 --------	June 1–15.
Apr. 15–June 1 ----	May 1–June 1 ------	May 10–June 1 ----	May 20–June 1.
Apr. 1–June 1 -----	Apr. 15–June 1 ----	May 1–June 15 ----	May 15–June 15.
May 10–June 1 ----	May 15–June 1 ----	May 20–June 1 ----	
Apr. 20–May 20 ----	May 1–June 1 -----	May 15–June 1 ----	May 15–June 15.
May 20–June 15 ---	June 1–15 ----------		
May 20–June 15 ---	June 1–15 ----------		
Apr. 15–May 15 ---	May 1–30 ----------	May 1–30 ----------	May 15–June 1.
Apr. 15–May 15 ---	May 1–30 ----------	May 1–30 ----------	May 15–June 1.
Apr. 1–May 1 ------	Apr. 15–May 15 ----	May 1–30 ----------	May 15–June 1.
Apr. 15–May 15 ----	Apr. 20–May 20 ----	May 1–30 ----------	May 15–June 1.
Apr. 10–May 1 -----	Apr. 20–May 10 ----	May 1–30 ----------	May 15–June 1.
Apr. 10–May 15 ----	Apr. 20–May 20 ----	May 1–30 ----------	May 15–June 1.
Apr. 15–May 15 ----	May 1–May 20 ----	May 1–15 ----------	May 1–15.
Apr. 15–May 15 ----	May 1–June 30 ----	May 10–June 30 ---	May 20–June 30.
Apr. 15–June 15 ---	May 1–June 30 ----	May 10–June 30 ---	May 20–June 30.
June 1–June 15 ----			
Apr. 15–June 1 ----	May 1–June 30 ----	May 10–June 30 ---	May 20–June 30.
May 20–June 10 ---	June 1–20 ----------		
Apr. 10–May 1 ----	Apr. 20–May 15 ----	May 1–30 ----------	May 10–June 10.
Apr. 1–May 1 ------	Apr. 20–May 15 ----	May 1–30 ----------	May 10–June 10.
Apr. 10–May 1 -----	Apr. 20–May 15 ----	May 1–30 ----------	May 10–June 10.
Apr. 15–May 15 ----	May 1–20 ----------	May 10–June 1 ----	May 20–June 10.
Apr. 15- May 15 ---	May 1–20 ----------	May 10–June 1 ----	May 20–June 10.
Apr. 1–May 15 -----	Apr. 15- June 1 ----	May 1–June 15 ----	May 10–June 15.
May 20–June 10 ---	May 25–June 15 ---	June 1–15 ---------	
Apr. 1–June 1 -----	Apr. 15–June 15 ---	May 1–June 15 ----	May 15–June 1.
Apr. 1–June 1 -----	Apr. 15–June 15 ---	May 1–June 15 ----	May 15–June 1.
Apr. 1–May 1 ------	Apr. 15–May 10 ----	May 1–20 ----------	May 15–June 1.
May 1–June 1 -----	May 1–20 ----------	May 10–20 ---------	May 20–June 1.
Apr. 15–June 1 ----	May 1–June 1 ------	May 10–June 1 ----	May 20–June 1.
Apr. 10–May 1 ----	Apr. 20–May 10 ----	May 1–June 1 -----	May 10–June 1.
Apr. 15–June 1 ----	May 1–June 1 ------	May 10–June 10 ---	May 20–June 10.
May 25–June 10 ---			
Apr. 1–June 15 ----	Apr. 10–June 15 ---	Apr. 20–June 15 ---	May 1–June 15.
May 10–June 15 ---	May 20–June 15 ---	June 1–15 ---------	
May 10–June 10 ---	May 20–June 15 ---	June 1–20 ---------	June 10–20.
May 15–June 10 ---	May 25–June 15 ---	June 5–20 ---------	June 15–30.
Apr. 1–June 1 -----	Apr. 15–June 1 ----	May 1–June 15 ----	May 15–June 15.
June 1–June 15 ----	June 15–July 1 ----		

Crop	Aug. 30	Sept. 10	Sept. 20	Sept. 30	Oct. 10	Oct. 20
Asparagus [1]					Oct. 20–Nov. 15	Nov. 1–Dec. 15.
Beans, lima				June 1–15	June 1–15	June 15–30.
Beans, snap	May 15–June 15	May 15–June 15	June 1–July 1	June 1–July 10	June 15–July 20	July 1–Aug. 1.
Beet	May 15–June 15	May 15–June 15	June 1–July 1	June 1–July 10	June 15–July 25	July 1–Aug. 5.
Broccoli, sprouting	May 1–June 1	May 1–June 1	May 1–June 15	June 1–30	June 15–July 15	July 1–Aug. 1.
Brussels sprouts	May 1–June 1	May 1–June 1	May 1–June 15	June 1–30	June 15–July 15	July 1–Aug. 1.
Cabbage [1]	May 1–June 1	May 1–June 1	May 1–June 15	June 1–July 10	June 1–July 15	July 1–20.
Cabbage, Chinese	May 15–June 15	May 15–June 15	June 1–July 1	June 1–July 15	June 15–Aug. 1	July 15–Aug. 15.
Carrot	May 15–June 15	May 15–June 15	June 1–July 1	June 1–July 10	June 1–July 20	June 15–Aug. 1.
Cauliflower [1]	May 1–June 1	May 1–July 1	May 1–July 1	May 10–July 15	June 1–July 25	July 1–Aug. 1.
Celery [1] and celeriac	May 1–June 1	May 1–June 1	May 15–July 1	June 1–July 5	June 1–July 15	July 1–Aug. 5.
Chard	May 1–June 15	May 15–July 1	June 1–July 1	June 1–July 5	June 1–July 20	June 1–Aug. 1.
Chervil and chives	May 10–June 10	May 1–June 15	May 15–June 15	(2)	(2)	(2)
Chicory, witloof	May 15–June 15	May 15–June 15	May 15–June 15	June 1–July 1	June 1–July 1	June 15–July 15.
Collards [1]	May 15–June 15	May 15–June 15	May 15–June 15	June 15–July 15	July 1–Aug. 1	July 15–Aug. 15.
Cornsalad	May 15–June 15	May 15–July 1	June 15–Aug. 1	July 15–Sept. 1	Aug. 15–Sept. 15	Sept. 1–Oct. 15.
Corn, sweet			June 1–July 1	June 1–July 1	June 1–July 10	June 1–July 20.
Cress, upland	May 15–June 15	May 15–July 1	June 15–Aug. 1	July 15–Sept. 15	Aug. 15–Sept. 15	Sept. 1–Oct. 15.
Cucumber			June 1–15	June 1–July 1	June 1–July 1	June 1–July 15.
Eggplant [1]				May 20–June 10	May 15–June 15	June 1–July 15.
Endive	June 1–July 1	June 1–July 1	June 15–July 15	June 15–Aug. 1	July 1–Aug. 15	July 15–Sept. 1.
Fennel, Florence	May 15–June 15	May 15–July 15	June 1–July 1	June 1–July 1	June 15–July 15	June 15–Aug. 1.
Garlic	(2)	(2)	(2)	(2)	(2)	(2)
Horseradish [1]	(2)	(2)	(2)	(2)	(2)	(2)
Kale	May 15–June 15	May 15–June 15	June 1–July 1	June 15–July 15	July 1–Aug. 1	July 15–Aug. 15.

Crop						
Kohlrabi	May 15-June 15	June 1-July 1	June 1-July 15	June 15-July 15	July 1-Aug. 1	July 15-Aug. 15.
Leek[1]	May 1-June 1	May 1-June 1	(2)			(2)
Lettuce, head[1]	May 15-July 1	May 15-July 1	June 1-July 1	June 15-Aug. 1	July 15-Aug. 15	Aug. 1-30.
Lettuce, leaf	May 15-July 15	May 15-July 15	June 1-Aug. 1	June 15-Aug. 1	July 15-Aug. 15	July 15-Sept. 1.
Muskmelon		May 15-July 15	June 1-June 20	May 20-June 20	June 1-June 15	June 15-July 20.
Mustard	May 15-July 15		June 1-July 1	June 1-July 1	July 15-Aug. 15	Aug. 1-Sept. 1.
Okra			June 1-20	June 1-20	June 1-July 15	June 1-Aug. 1.
Onion[1]	May 1-June 10	May 1-June 10	(2)	(2)	(2)	
Onion, seed	May 1-June 1	May 1-June 10	(2)	(2)	(2)	(2)
Onion, sets	May 1-June 10	May 1-June 10	(2)	(2)	(2)	(2)
Parsley	May 15-June 15	May 1-June 15	June 1-July 1	June 15-Aug. 1	June 15-Aug. 1	(2)
Parsnip	May 15-June 15	May 15-June 15	May 15-June 15	June 1-July 10	June 1-July 10	
Peas, garden	May 10-June 15	May 1-June 15	June 1-July 15	(2)	(2)	July 15-Aug. 15.
Peas, black-eye		May 1-July 1		June 1-July 1	June 1-July 1	
Pepper[1]	May 15-June 1	May 1-June 15	June 1-June 20	June 1-July 1	June 1-July 1	(2)
Potato	May 1-July 15	May 1-Aug. 1	May 1-June 15	May 15-June 15	July 15-Sept. 1	June 1-July 1.
Radish	Sept. 1-Oct. 15	Sept. 15-Oct. 15	Sept. 15-Nov. 1	Oct. 1-Nov. 1	Oct. 15-Nov. 15	June 1-July 10.
Rhubarb[1]	May 15-June 15	May 1-June 15	May 1-June 15		June 15-July 15	June 15-July 15.
Rutabaga	May 15-June 1	May 10-June 10	May 20-June 20	June 15-July 15	June 15-July 15	Aug. 1-Oct. 1.
Salsify	(2)	(2)	June 1-20	June 15-July 15	June 15-July 15	Oct. 15-Dec. 1.
Shallot	May 15-June 15	May 1-June 15	(2)	(2)	(2)	July 10-20.
Sorrel			June 1-July 1	June 1-July 1	June 1-July 1	June 1-July 1.
Soybean	May 15-July 1	June 1-July 15	June 1-July 15	July 1-Aug. 1	July 1-Aug. 1	(2)
Spinach			May 25-June 10	Aug. 1-Sept. 1	Aug. 1-Sept. 1	July 15-Aug. 15.
Spinach, New Zealand	June 10-20	June 1-20	July 1-Aug. 15	June 1-Aug. 1	June 1-Aug. 1	June 1-July 5.
Squash, summer			May 15-July 1	June 1-July 15	June 1-July 15	Aug. 20-Sept. 10.
Squash, winter			May 15-July 1	June 1-July 1	June 1-July 1	June 1-Aug. 1.
Sweetpotato	June 20-30		May 20-June 10	May 20-June 10	May 20-June 10	June 1-July 20.
Tomato	May 15-June 15	June 10-20	June 1-20	June 1-20	June 1-20	June 1-July 1.
Turnip		June 1-July 1	June 1-Aug. 1	July 1-Aug. 1	July 1-Aug. 1	July 15-Aug. 15.
Watermelon		June 1-July 1	May 15-June 1	June 1-June 15	June 1-June 15	June 15-July 20.

[1] Plants.

[2] Generally spring-planted (table 4).

Crop	Oct. 30	Nov. 10	Nov. 20	Nov. 30	Dec. 10	Dec. 20
Asparagus [1]	Nov. 15–Jan. 1	Dec. 1–Jan. 1				
Beans, lima	July 1–Aug. 1	July 1–Aug. 15	July 15–Sept. 1	Aug. 1–Sept. 15	Sept. 1–30	Sept. 1–Oct. 1.
Beans, snap	July 1–Aug. 15	July 1–Sept. 1	July 1–Sept. 10	Aug. 15–Sept. 20	Sept. 1–30	Sept. 1–Nov. 1.
Beet	Aug. 1–Sept. 1	Aug. 1–Oct. 1	Sept. 1–Dec. 1	Sept. 1–Dec. 15	Sept. 1–Dec. 31	Sept. 1–Dec. 31.
Broccoli, sprouting	July 1–Aug. 15	Aug. 1–Sept. 1	Aug. 1–Sept. 15	Aug. 1–Oct. 1	Aug. 1–Nov. 1	Sept. 1–Dec. 31.
Brussels sprouts	July 1–Aug. 15	Aug. 1–Sept. 1	Aug. 1–Sept. 15	Aug. 1–Oct. 1	Aug. 1–Nov. 1	Sept. 1–Dec. 31.
Cabbage [1]	Aug. 1–Sept. 1	Sept. 1–15	Sept. 1–Dec. 1	Sept. 1–Dec. 31	Sept. 1–Dec. 31	Sept. 1–Dec. 31.
Cabbage, Chinese	Aug. 1–Sept. 15	Aug. 15–Oct. 1	Sept. 1–Oct. 15	Sept. 15–Dec. 1	Sept. 1–Nov. 15	Sept. 1–Dec. 1.
Carrot	July 1–Aug. 15	Aug. 1–Sept. 1	Sept. 1–Nov. 1	Sept. 15–Dec. 1	Sept. 15–Dec. 1	Sept. 15–Dec. 1.
Cauliflower [1]	July 15–Aug. 15	Aug. 1–Sept. 1	Aug. 1–Sept. 15	Sept. 15–Oct. 10	Sept. 1–Oct. 20	Sept. 15–Nov. 1.
Celery [1] and celeriac	June 15–Aug. 15	July 1–Aug. 15	July 15–Sept. 15	Aug. 15–Oct. 15	Sept. 1–Oct. 20	Oct. 1–Dec. 31.
Chard	June 1–Sept. 10	June 1–Sept. 15	June 1–Oct. 1	Aug. 1–Dec. 1	June 1–Dec. 1	June 1–Dec. 31.
Chervil and chives	(2)	(2)	Nov. 1–Dec. 31	Nov. 1–Dec. 31	Nov. 1–Dec. 31	Nov. 1–Dec. 31.
Chicory, witloof	July 1–Aug. 10	July 10–Aug. 20	July 20–Sept. 1	Aug. 15–Sept. 30	Aug. 15–Oct. 15	Aug. 15–Oct. 15.
Collards [1]	Aug. 1–Sept. 15	Aug. 15–Oct. 1	Aug. 25–Nov. 1	Sept. 1–Dec. 1	Sept. 1–Dec. 31	Sept. 1–Dec. 31.
Cornsalad	Sept. 15–Nov. 1	Oct. 1–Dec. 1	Oct. 1–Dec. 1	Oct. 1–Dec. 31	Oct. 1–Dec. 31	Oct. 1–Dec. 31.
Corn, sweet	June 1–Aug. 1	June 1–Aug. 15	June 1–Sept. 1			
Cress, upland	Sept. 15–Nov. 1	Oct. 1–Dec. 1	Oct. 1–Dec. 1	Oct. 1–Dec. 31	Oct. 1–Dec. 31	Oct. 1–Dec. 31.
Cucumber	June 1–Aug. 1	June 1–Aug. 15	June 1–Aug. 15	July 15–Sept. 15	Aug. 15–Oct. 1	Aug. 15–Oct. 1.
Eggplant [1]	June 1–July 1	June 1–July 15	June 1–Aug. 1	July 1–Sept. 1	Aug. 1–Sept. 30	Aug. 1–Sept. 30.
Endive	July 15–Aug. 15	Aug. 1–Sept. 1	Sept. 1–Oct. 1	Sept. 1–Nov. 15	Sept. 1–Nov. 15	Sept. 1–Dec. 31.
Fennel, Florence	July 1–Aug. 1	July 15–Aug. 15	Aug. 15–Sept. 15	Sept. 1–Nov. 15	Sept. 1–Dec. 1	Sept. 1–Dec. 1.
Garlic	(2)	Aug. 1–Oct. 1	Aug. 15–Oct. 1	Sept. 1–Nov. 15	Sept. 15–Nov. 15	Sept. 15–Nov. 15.
Horseradish [1]	(2)	(2)	(2)	(2)	(2)	(2)
Kale	July 15–Sept. 1	Aug. 1–Sept. 15	Aug. 15–Oct. 15	Sept. 1–Dec. 1	Sept. 1–Dec. 31	Sept. 1–Dec. 31.

Kohlrabi	Aug. 1–Sept. 1	Aug. 15–Sept. 15	Sept. 1–Oct. 15	Sept. 1–Dec. 1	Sept. 1–Dec. 31
Leek[1]	(2)	(2)	Sept. 1–Nov. 1	Sept. 1–Nov. 1	Sept. 15–Nov. 1
Lettuce, head[1]	Aug. 1–Sept. 15	Aug. 15–Oct. 15	Sept. 1–Nov. 1	Sept. 1–Nov. 1	Sept. 15–Dec. 31
Lettuce, leaf	Aug. 15–Oct. 1	Aug. 25–Oct. 1	Sept. 1–Nov. 1	Sept. 1–Dec. 1	Sept. 15–Dec. 31
Muskmelon	July 1–July 15	July 15–July 30			
Mustard	Aug. 15–Oct. 15	Aug. 15–Nov. 1	Sept. 1–Dec. 1	Sept. 1–Dec. 1	Sept. 15–Dec. 1
Okra	June 1–Aug. 10	June 1–Aug. 20	June 1–Sept. 10	June 1–Sept. 20	Aug. 1–Oct. 1
Onion[1]		Sept. 1–Oct. 15	Oct. 1–Dec. 31	Oct. 1–Dec. 31	Oct. 1–Dec. 31
Onion, seed			Sept. 1–Nov. 1	Sept. 1–Nov. 1	Sept. 15–Nov. 1
Onion, sets		Oct. 1–Dec. 1	Nov. 1–Dec. 31	Nov. 1–Dec. 31	Nov. 1–Dec. 31
Parsley	Aug. 1–Sept. 15	Sept. 1–Nov. 15	Aug. 1–Sept. 1	Sept. 1–Dec. 1	Sept. 1–Dec. 31
Parsnip	(2)	(2)	Oct. 1–Dec. 1	Sept. 1–Nov. 15	Sept. 1–Dec. 1
Peas, garden	Aug. 1–Sept. 15	Sept. 1–Nov. 1	Oct. 1–Dec. 1	Oct. 1–Dec. 1	Oct. 1–Dec. 31
Peas, black-eye	June 1–Aug. 1	June 15–Aug. 15	July 1–Sept. 1	July 1–Sept. 10	July 1–Sept. 20
Pepper[1]	June 1–July 20	June 1–Aug. 1	June 1–Aug. 15	June 15–Sept. 1	Aug. 15–Oct. 1
Potato	July 20–Aug. 10	July 25–Aug. 20	Aug. 10–Sept. 15	Aug. 1–Sept. 15	Aug. 1–Sept. 15
Radish	Aug. 15–Oct. 15	Sept. 1–Nov. 15	Sept. 1–Dec. 1	Sept. 1–Dec. 31	Oct. 1–Dec. 31
Rhubarb[1]	Nov. 1–Dec. 1				
Rutabaga	July 15–Aug. 1	July 15–Aug. 15	Aug. 1–Sept. 1	Sept. 1–Nov. 15	Oct. 15–Nov. 15
Salsify	June 1–July 10	June 15–July 20	July 15–Aug. 15	Aug. 15–Sept. 30	Sept. 1–Oct. 31
Shallot	(2)	Aug. 1–Oct. 1	Aug. 15–Oct. 1	Aug. 15–Oct. 1	Sept. 15–Nov. 1
Sorrel	Aug. 1–Sept. 15	Aug. 15–Oct. 1	Aug. 15–Oct. 15	Sept. 1–Nov. 15	Sept. 1–Dec. 31
Soybean	June 1–July 15	June 1–July 25	June 1–July 30	June 1–July 30	June 1–July 30
Spinach	Sept. 1–Oct. 1	Sept. 15–Nov. 1	Oct. 1–Dec. 1	Oct. 1–Dec. 31	Oct. 1–Dec. 31
Spinach, New Zealand	June 1–Aug. 15	June 1–Aug. 15	June 1–Aug. 15	June 1–Sept. 1	June 1–Oct. 1
Squash, summer	June 1–Aug. 1	June 1–Aug. 10	June 1–Aug. 20	July 15–Aug. 15	Aug. 1–Sept. 1
Squash, winter	June 10–July 10	June 20–July 20	July 1–Aug. 1	July 15–Aug. 1	June 1–July 1
Sweetpotato	June 1–15	June 1–July 1	June 1–July 1	June 1–July 1	June 1–July 1
Tomato	June 1–July 1	June 1–July 15	June 1–Aug. 1	Aug. 1–Sept. 1	Aug. 15–Oct. 1
Turnip	Aug. 1–Sept. 15	Sept. 1–Oct. 15	Sept. 1–Nov. 1	Sept. 1–Nov. 15	Oct. 1–Dec. 31
Watermelon	July 1–July 15	July 15–July 30	Sept. 1–Nov. 15		

[1] Plants.
[2] Generally spring-planted (table 4).

Correcting Alkaline Soils

To bring soils toward neutral pH is the usual desire of most of us, as most vegetable crops, and many, many ornamentals and house plants do best in such soils. But acidity is not the only possible problem. In large areas of this continent, the soil is too alkaline, or sweet, for good plant growth. While plants will tolerate a certain degree of soil sweetness, they will *not* grow well if alkalinity even approaches the reverse degree of acidity, in most cases. In other words, while a one point acid soil (6.0 pH) will serve to grow a vegetable such as potatoes, the tubers will die if the soil approaches a one point alkalinity rating (8.0 pH). Of course, this is an extreme example, as potatoes do best in very acid soils anyway (with a pH preference from 4.8 to 6.5). But above 8.0 pH, just about nothing grows well. The need, then, to correct alkaline soils is obvious. We'll occasionally find that overliming has made a previously too-acid soil too alkaline: this problem is most likely to occur on light, sandy soils, where proper testing procedures have not been followed. In any case, correction is needed in order to get the best growth from plants.

Organic Matter

The major way to correct for an overalkaline soil is simply to add organic matter to the soil — humus, mulches, compost. Certain types of mulch will continue to keep soils in balance for years, with little variation in either direction. Generally, a hay mulch in the garden will prevent problems with either acidity or alkalinity, keeping the soil almost determinedly neutral. In cases where the soil is heavily alkaline, you can increase the effectiveness of the treatment by applying such things as tree leaves (pine needles, or the needles from most any conifer, are heavily acid and so, in a partially decomposed state, will do a quick and effective job of curing oversweet soils), sawdust, wood chips. Almost all trees prefer acid soils and take on those characteristics from the soil, so that using such material in a thick layer will quickly change the most alkaline soil towards neutral. Of course, too heavy an application of wood chips will then kick the soil test to the acid side and force you to liming! It's easy to see why before and after tests are valuable, if not exactly essential. (After all, our grandparents and their parents fed an awful lot of large families without having the chemical testing aids we have today: but it is easier and quicker our way.)

Too much fertilizer can be as harmful as too little, but there is seldom any possibility of getting too much humus, decayed and decaying organic matter, into your soil, though if you do use immense amounts of tree wastes (leaves, wood chips, bark), you will find the soil going strongly acid sooner or later. This is easily prevented either by balancing the compost used or by adding lime.

Composts

Natural compost forms the humus layer in all soils that nature developed. Man-made compost is probably the single best fertilizer, and almost always the cheapest, we can use in tending plants today. A good compost pile will contain all the nutrients any plant needs, along with a generous share of the needed worm, microorganic, and other life necessary to maintain soil balance and fertility. With the addition of certain types of waste, the compost pile can also be made to be useful in balancing soils that go heavily in one direction or the other on the pH scale.

Compost for the garden can be made in several ways, using pits, piles, special frames, or purchased holders. For most of us, a pit or a pile is probably the best bet, since special frames and boughten stuff tend to run the expense up.

Making Compost

The making of compost is not difficult, but it does involve doing a few things to help speed up decomposition and to reduce the entire amount of physical labor. Your first step will depend a great deal on your location and on how much compost you expect to need. A huge flower or vegetable garden will require a lot of compost, whereas a small garden won't need so much. On the other hand, a small garden will usually be located in neighborhoods where you may well need to disguise the compost bin or pit it to prevent complaints from neighbors. Properly made compost, by the way, will not have an offensive odor, nor will it draw flies. Generally, early and middle fall is the best time to make compost in most areas of the United States and Canada, though the subtropical areas offer year-round composting opportunities just as they do year-round growing seasons. Compost, though, can be made at any time of the year, anywhere. What makes winter composting best is that it allows plenty of time for the decomposition. Much organic matter, and a wide variety, too, will be on hand or easily found at this time. Next, the compost will be ready to use just as you are getting ready to start spring planting. And in some areas, winter compost will not suffer from the problems of dryness that develop at other times of the year. A compost pile must remain moist to work.

So dig your compost pit and place a few concrete blocks around the bottom for ventilation. Good ventilation of the pile of organic matter is essential, because the microorganisms that do the work are all aerobic and require much oxygen to do their jobs. If the pile or pit is to be a large one, you might consider setting fence posts inside the pile, slipping their ends into the concrete block holes, or simply driving them into the ground. When the pile reaches its preplanned height (no more than five feet for maximum decomposition speed), you yank the poles out, automatically providing ventilating shafts.

For winter composting, some sort of nonfreezing material should be used as a heat retention cover for the compost. Burlap serves very well, as do many of the plastic sheets readily available. Even unfrozen soil can be used, as can a very thick covering of leaves.

Compost Components

The organic gardener's cry states that garbage is very valuable. In composting that is very certainly the truth. Your compost pile can be made up of just about anything that can be expected to decay under conditions of dampness, heat, and bacterial action: apple cores, eggshells, bones, coffee grounds, meat trimmings, vegetable parings, leaves, grass clippings, manure.

For best results, the pile of compost should not reach higher than five feet. The width can vary from five to ten feet, and the length can be whatever you wish. This follows Sir Albert Howard's method of composting, including using the posts as aerators.

Start with a layer of green material such as grass clippings, making that layer about one foot deep. Then add a couple of inches of manure, or sewage sludge if that is more easily available. Stick in the aeration posts (use pipe if posts are hard to come by), and continue with similar layers on up the pile until you reach five feet. Cover it with burlap, soil, or other such material to help retain heat and prevent too rapid evaporation of water. If you wish, you can tamp the heap slightly, making a depression in the center, or for larger heaps several along the edges and in the center, to catch and hold some rainwater. Then just turn twice. By the time spring ground preparation is upon you, the compost heap will be ready. At that time, you simply spread a couple of inches of the compost on your garden, till it in, and go on about your planting.

Leaves: Though superb for compost, they take a long time to decay if used as the only content of a green layer. Shred them fine if possible.

Hay: Young, green hay is best, but any hay is heavy in nitrogen. Shred when possible.

Sawdust, wood chips, bark: Sprinkle sawdust in lightly or it won't decompose completely. (It tends to pack and prevent the passage of air, which is essential to decomposition.) Wood chips and bark can be added much the same as any other material, but it is wise to keep in mind that, as the wood decays, the pile of organic matter will become more acid.

Stalks, weeds, garden trimmings: Add it all, cut or shredded as fine as possible. If the compost pile decays with enough heat, the seeds from the weeds will decompose and present no problem in the garden.

Grass clippings: Grass clippings are fine in compost. (They also make good mulch.)

Garbage: Don't use soapy water and fats in compost. Other than that, just about all kitchen waste makes an excellent addition to your green layers. As long as the pile is heating properly, you can even include hard-to-break-down material, such as bones and eggshells, and not have to worry about them.

The list of materials that can be added to a compost heap is very large; only their availability in your locale will act as limits. Manure, of course, is always an excellent addition; in fact, it makes a much better fertilizer if it is composted. (This is especially so of horse manure, which is strong enough to burn plants if it is spread when fresh.) If sewage sludge is available in your community, it can be used to replace the manure layer in your compost. Should you have a local leather-working shop, you might try to obtain scraps and dust from them, since leathers are very high in both nitrogen and phosphorus. Where shelled corn is produced, you may find literally tons of corncobs; and in nut country it is often possible to find shells piled up waiting to be hauled away. Use a bit of imagination and you can probably locate good sources of extra material for your compost in several spots around your locale. Even city food stores trim and discard vegetable waste each day. Picking up this otherwise wasted material can really increase the size of a compost heap. Cities, towns, counties, power companies all take down many trees a year, often running the wood through a chipper that produces material nearly ideal for composting. Sawmills may be surrounded by huge mounds of sawdust. Compost is all around us, just asking to be added to the working heap.

Getting the Compost to Work

Start your compost by watering each layer. It will work as long as it is damp and protected from cold to the extent that natural decay can provide the heat necessary to the life and activity of the microorganisms that do the work of breaking down the materials. Dampness is an essential. A compost pile should be ever moist, though not always drenched. Earthworms will almost naturally gravitate to such a pile, but if they do not, it may well pay you to add, to your first batch, a few pounds of earthworms at the outside edges. (The very high heat at the center of the compost heap will either kill or drive away any earthworms: though you can moderate the heat by turning the heap more frequently, it's usually easier simply to add the earthworms at the perimeters of the pile.)

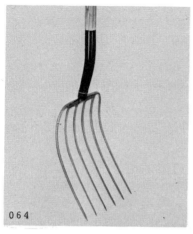

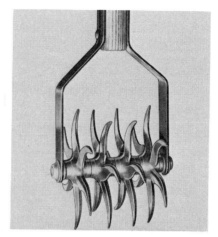

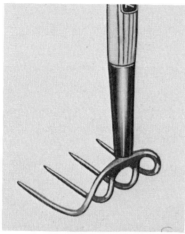

Fig. 4-5. (Top, left) Pitchfork Used to Turn Small Compost Heap.

Fig. 4-6. (Top, right) Rotary Tine Cultivator for All Types of Soil.

Fig. 4-7. (Left) Spading Fork.

Fig. 4-8. (Bottom, left) Steel Bow Rake.

Fig. 4-9. (Bottom, right) Basic Hoe. (Photos courtesy of True Temper)

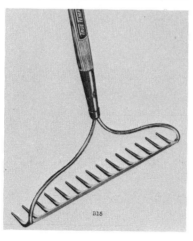

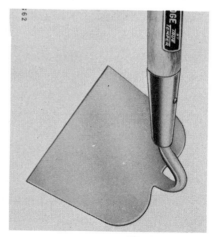

Additions to Compost

To more completely follow the methods of Howard, you can
add a very thin layer of topsoil over the manure layer, and then
add another thin layer, this time of wood ash, granite dust, or
a similar mineral substance. To correct for high acidity, a thin
sprinkling of lime can be used, a good idea when you've used
a great many wood waste products in building the compost
heap. Otherwise, a highly acid compost pile can be used to
more quickly balance high alkaline soils.

About two weeks after the capping of the compost heap,
you will want to take a shot at turning the material. For small
heaps, use a pitchfork to move the outer parts of the pile into
the center. Repeat this procedure two or three weeks later.
This ensures that all material is affected by the high internal
temperatures, while also serving to bring those temperatures
down from an initial 150° F. to about 125° or 130° after the
first turning. To turn a large compost heap almost always requires machinery or a major physical effort. (Fig. 4-5)

A compost heap made in this way will finish in three to
five months. To obtain a constant supply you can simply
start a new heap as soon as the old one has been capped and
has started working. By completing a heap every two months,
you should be able to compost steadily throughout the year,
no matter whether you are working in flower gardens, vegetable gardens, or simply dressing the soil around trees.

Quick Composting

Rapid-finish composts can be made with the fourteen-day
method developed by the University of California Department
of Sanitary Engineering. All material *must* be shredded or
ground fine. A good way to work this with leaves and other

light materials is simply to make a pile of the stuff, and take the rotary lawnmower through it several times. (Use the catch bag on the lawnmower, or you may end up chasing particles all over the place!) Make a heap, without layering, about five feet high and of a size in its other dimensions that can be handled reasonably. Wet it down. Turn the pile after three days, and turn it every two days after that. The compost will be rougher, not as crumbly, as that made by Howard's method, but it will be, after about two weeks, perfectly suitable for use in your garden. In actuality, the feel or crumbliness of the compost has little direct bearing on its value as a fertilizer. In some areas, so many of the nutrients are leached out of a long-standing compost pile that the compost made by the fourteen-day method is appreciably richer.

Green Manuring

Green manuring is a simple process, one part of a larger process known to farmers as sheet composting. A farmer will often plant soy beans, clover, or other forage plants having a high nitrogen content, allow it to reach partial maturity, and then till it under. While this is an ideal method for some farmers, it isn't of great value to the home gardener, for the land in green manure is actually taken out of production until the plants reach the point where they're turned under. I mention it here only because of its possible value to those of you who may wish to till successive plots, planting one this year, and the other the next. For complete details of the method, consult your county extension agent. He can advise you of the best and cheapest plants to use in your area.

Mulch

Mulch is the basic tool that can help make of most kinds of
gardening, if not a lazy person's refuge, then at least an indo-
lent's delight. For some forty or more years, Ruth Stout used
what she called her no-work gardening method. Miss Stout's
basic, non-secret garden ingredient was the heavy and extensive use of various mulching materials (*The Ruth Stout No-
Work Garden Book*, Bantam Books, 1971). In fact, she claims
for her method that mulch will cure or alleviate just about
every garden problem and prevent the need for composting,
fertilizing, most watering, tilling, and just about every other
chore that we all associate with gardening of most kinds. And
a lot of this is, purely and simply, the plain truth. But as to
the elimination of composting and some of the other claims,
I leave you to try the mulching method yourself. Then make
your own decision. In any case, if you start with poor soil,
mulch is not enough, as it takes years to break down into a
good, deep humus layer. But in the prevention of drought
damage, cutting out the need for weeding and extensive cultivating and other such benefits, there can be no argument what-
soever. Mulch is the small gardener's best friend.

In its simplest form, mulch is a covering of organic, or non-
organic, material that is laid between plants and rows. As I've
already said, grass clippings make a top-quality mulch, though
they are seldom available in the quantity needed. I always use
them with straw or other organic materials. Hay and straw are
other top mulch materials. For economy it is best to look for
supplies at the end of harvest seasons, or even before the growing season, among leftover stock. The straw may be moldy,
but that's fine for mulching purposes, and will bring the price
of each bale down by no less than 50 percent of the local market price. Sometimes moldy hay or straw can be had for the
hauling.

Both grass clippings and hay need to be applied to a reasonable depth if growth is to be prevented: try at least three inches of grass clippings and three times that much or more of straw or hay. (If, however, the straw or hay is shredded first, three inches should be enough.) For fall mulches, look to the leaves on your lawn that have not already gone into the compost pile. Such nitrogen-rich material is excellent for mulching. If possible, shred leaves before using them as a mulch because whole leaves have a tendency to pack down into a soggy mass that inhibits aeration of the soil.

Sawdust is not a good mulch for most plants. It lacks the nitrogen needed, and is often very highly acid. It is ideal for plants, such as potatoes and sweet potatoes, which require a strongly acid soil. In such cases, though, the nitrogen deficiency should be made up, either by using a good rich compost or by mixing in fertilizers rich in nitrogen.

The list of mulches can go on and on. For years, I used newspapers under a layer of grass clippings and straw. (I avoided using the colored sections, since the ink is reputed to be a bit poisonous, and no one seems to know the effect on plants.) This lets you cut down on the depth of the grass or straw while at the same time eliminating the need to weight the newspapers up with boards, bricks, or stones to keep them from blowing away when dry. Newspaper mulches should be tilled in every fall and, for best results, renewed in spring.

Peat moss and bark chips of various ornamental woods are often used in flower gardens, but tend to be far too expensive for use in food gardens of any but the smallest size. In a lot of gardens, black plastic is used as mulch, either as strips laid between plant rows or oevr the entire garden with appropriate size holes cut or punched for the plants. Plastic does an excellent job of providing the water- and heat-retention qualities needed from mulches, but it adds nothing to the richness of the soil. Its advatnage is that it lasts indefinitely, but, at the

same time, it is a petroleum product, and so uses up one of
the earth's nonrenewable resources for a job done better, if
not more easily, by other, renewable materials.

Time to Mulch

According to Ruth Stout, the mulch can be laid down and left
there, year round. She used to simply push back the mulch in
order to pop seeds into the damp, warm earth. This is possible
with a very deep layer of mulch because the soil stays con-
stantly loose underneath and seldom, if ever, requires tilling.
But the mulch breaks down only slowly each year and takes a
long time to add nutrients to the soil. For soils that need en-
riching, it is better to till the mulch under each year, and renew
it in the spring, immediately after the seeds are planted. In
some cases, as with potatoes, you apply mulch all over the
seedlings, and cover those only very lightly, if at all, with soil.
The result is a large harvest, and a harvest that is easy to make,
since you don't have to dig into the rows to get at the potatoes. Simply pick them from under the mulch!

Transplanted stock, such as tomatoes and peppers, should
be mulched as soon as it is planted in the garden. Keep the
mulch well back from the stalks until the plants have a good
start.

Actually, my preference in most cases is to mulch the entire garden as soon as the earliest plants are in. The mulch
will help to retain the heat that has already accumulated and
will help retain water, keeping the ground nicely moist for
planting. (Leaving mulch on a garden over the winter tends to
delay planting a bit, since the insulation keeps the ground from
warming up quite as rapidly as unmulched ground; that is a
major reason why I prefer to till it under each year.)

Benefits of Mulch

Obviously, an organic mulch serves to feed the soil. In a sense, organic mulches are a form of sheet composting. A good, thick layer òf mulch will prevent the growth of weeds, cutting down on the root competition that can stunt the growth of useful plants. Mulch also keeps the soil soft and moist, as water doesn't have the surface area needed for rapid evaporation, and the soil is not pounded down by wind and rain and feet, but is, instead, cushioned and protected.

Cultivation and Tilling

Cultivation refers in general to all the processes of preparing soil for planting. What we are most concerned with here, though, is the process known as tilling. Most of us will not be working with immense gang plows of the rotary and blade types, so we basically come down to either hand or rotary tilling to prepare soil for planting. We are looking primarily to aerate the soil, not to pulverize it, so that tilling is done carefully, but not so extensively that the soil can be passed through a fine mesh screen. Many soils that tend toward clay types will clump badly if broken down into small particles, and sandy soils will often just allow most nutrients to leach out when turned to near powder. (Fig. 4-6)

Breaking the soil up by hand is practicable for small gardens, and it is easiest to turn in soils having a sand base. Using a spading fork or a spade shovel, turn the grass or other organic matter on top under to a depth of about ten inches, and then break up the large clods. (Fig. 4-7)

Rotary tillers are practical for the home gardener only when there is a rather large expanse of garden to work, for the cost can run anywhere from $175 up to more than $650. Still, such tillers are highly efficient. If used properly, they do a much better job in many areas than you can do by hand, with a great deal less effort, and a lot of time saved. In many cases, you can hire someone to till the garden for you, at a reasonable cost. Or you can buy a tiller and rent it (and yourself) out to till other people's gardens, so recovering a part of the cost of the tiller.

Rotary tillers work well when breaking up new grass for use as garden plots, as they chop the grass and its roots up quite fine, adding to the humus layer. The same ability is useful in chopping up such things as corn stalks and other vegetable matter during the fall tilling. All of this adds to the layer of organic matter. The finely chopped material decomposes readily, which is of great benefit in building any garden.

On top of all this, later cultivation between rows in unmulched gardens is much easier, as you simply place the rows of plants far enough apart to allow the tiller to be run through, and save all the effort of hand tilling and cultivating during the growing season. Weeds are chopped and added to the humus layer. In general, though, if the garden is of reasonable size, mulching is probably a better way to keep down weeds, as it also provides a method of keeping water in the soil during dry periods, as well as preventing too much heat from building up during those very hot summer days.

Tilling should be done at a time when the soil is moderately damp. Tilling when it is too dry will simply cause soil to blow away, and will raise the underlayers to where they, too, can dry out rapidly. Tilling when the soil is far too wet, especially early in the spring, will cause you to have a garden that looks as if it were made of adobe bricks — unless the soil is very sandy.

Telling whether or not the soil is ready for tilling is simpler than many books make it sound. To test for wetness, pick up a handful of soil from the dampest area in your garden and about six inches down. Squeeze it in your hand. If the soil clumps into one or more large lumps, it is still too wet to work with. Give it a few more days to dry out. To test for dryness, pick up a smaller handful and blow on the soil as hard as you can. If more than a few bits of dust fly off, then the soil is too dry to be worked. You have a choice here: wait for rain, or water the garden. If you choose the latter, water heavily enough to provide good penetration and to prevent evaporation. Either can cause problems when you till the next day.

Watering the Garden

As we have said, watering the garden is best done in the cool of the evening. But the amount of water is just as important as the time and temperature of the water in relation to the soil temperature. In most areas you will need an amount of water equivalent to about an inch of rain, according to the U.S. Department of Agriculture. That's a lot of water, on the order of 900 gallons simply for a 30 by 50 foot garden plot. Don't bother with light sprinklings daily. A light sprinkling will not penetrate to the depth needed to provide sufficient storage water for the rest of the week, and much will be lost by evaporation. Do a good job of soaking things down once a week and you will get much better results. Soak the soil very well between rows, or between plants. If you also conserve water by mulching, you can probably reduce the weekly watering to once every two weeks, or even once every three weeks.

Garden Tools

For the average small garden, whether ornamental or vegetable, you won't need a great many tools. For this reason, I recommend that you go out and buy the best you can find of the types you need. Quality tools and a small amount of care, such as regular cleaning of spading fork tines and periodic linseeding of wooden handles, will mean you will not be likely to have to replace the tools in a normal lifetime. One spading fork I have has been used by two generations of my family — and mistreated by both by being left out in the weather. The handle has been treated exactly twice with boiled linseed oil. Still, though this tool is well over twenty-five years old, it has its original handle and is perfectly useful. At the time my parents bought it, the fork was the finest available.

Get a spading fork, even if you plan to have the garden rotary-tilled. You'll also need a steel bow rake and a common hoe. A length of mason's cord for laying out plant rows is also very handy. A wheelbarrow of the type used by building contractors is a good investment for most gardens: avoid those lightweight "gardening" wheelbarrows totally. While they may cost less than a third what a good contractor's wheelbarrow does, they last about one tenth as long. A substitute for a wheelbarrow can be found in the carts sold by Garden Way Research. They are more easily pulled, tilted, pushed, and so on, and will carry much bulkier loads than will a wheelbarrow. These are also expensive, but they are available more cheaply as kits that you assemble. (Figs. 4-8, 4-9)

Garden hose is a somewhat different story. Some of the cheaper hoses will last as long as the more expensive ones, but — they will also drive you half crazy. You have never had so much fun at gardening as you will have on the chilly day (under 45° F.) when you try to uncoil a cheap plastic garden hose. For durability, there's little to choose in normal use (get the most expensive garden hose you can afford if it is going to be badly mistreated), but the cool weather use of a good hose is much easier. Get at least a 5/8 inch inside-diameter garden hose so that water pressure remains decent. Whatever else you get, find a solid brass nozzle for your garden hose. There are literally dozens of nozzles on the market, from plastic to tin to rubber. Brass is by far the best. Though it is most expensive, it will outlast by years any other kind.

For large gardens, rotary tillers and even garden tractors are helpful. Here the selection really depends on available cash. Simply flipping through a recent Montgomery Ward suburban catalog shows a price range for garden tractors that ends only when it has hit $2,139, plus shipping and local taxes. (That price includes no attachments. You must add the cost of each one to figure your total investment.) So make sure you really need this expensive tool before you spring to buy it. Admittedly, the usefulness of small garden tractors is immense, as they can pull rotary tillers and lawn mowers up to four feet wide; and, with proper attachments, they can be used as front-end loaders, compost material shredders, snowblowers and snow plows, sweepers, manure and fertilizer spreaders, planters, lawn rollers, haulers, and so on.

Rotary tillers have nearly as wide a range of prices. Those having rear-mounted tines are generally more expensive than the front-mounted units. I have to admit to a basic and strong prejudice here. I strongly prefer the models with rear-mounted tines. They are much less strenuous to use. They till up their own tracks. And, usually, depth control is easier with rear-mounted tines. If the tiller you buy is a heavy-duty model, make sure it has a reverse gear, or you will do more work turning the tiller at garden corners than you would if you hand-tilled the garden.

Chapter 5

ROOTS

In the foregoing sections, we have covered the habitat of roots and how to provide the best possible soils for most root systems, but that is not all there is to it. While the root environment has a strong effect on how well roots grow, and thus on how well the plant grows overall, the heredity of the plant has as much effect. For instance, there is no way a bulbous storage root, such as a potato, can put down the long, long, root system of, say, a cornstalk. In fact, root systems are so different from plant to plant that it is often possible to classify the plant by its underground life structure alone. And the growth of roots varies greatly, even among similar plants. For example, samples of winter rye taken in the field will offer about 150 roots to the cubic inch, whereas Kentucky blue grass may have as many as 2,000 roots in the same volume of soil! To this number must be added the root hairs. Root hairs vary in size, according to plant type, but they usually measure about 1/2000 of an inch in diameter and under 1/125 of an inch long. Our winter rye could have some 250,000 root hairs, or even more, and the bluegrass could offer about four times that many. (Fig. 5-1, 5-2)

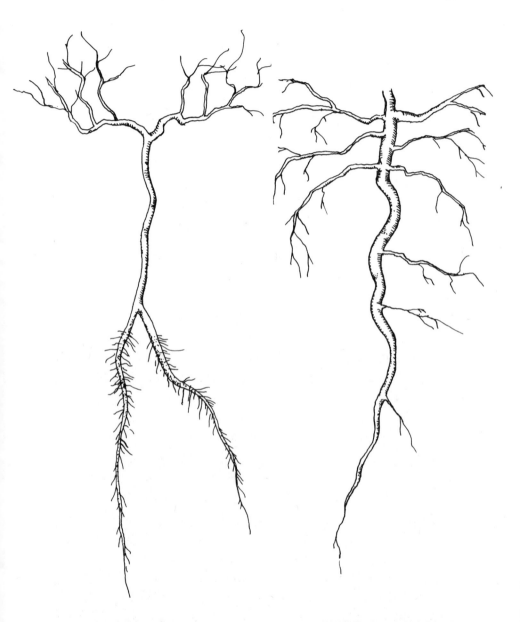

Fig. 5-1. Root System of
Chrysothamnus Nauseosus
Showing Long Taproot
and Secondary Roots on
the Primary Root

Fig. 5-2. Root System of
Franseria Acanthicarpa
Showing Penetrating Tap-
root and Numerous
Secondary Roots

Root Formation

Each day, a living plant sends out new roots and root hairs in a continuing search for the life-sustaining soil water and the nutrients held in it.

When the seed we plant starts to germinate, the primary root of the plant is the first part pushed out. From this primary root, secondary roots move out into the soil, and then become part of the primary root system, which continues to send out lateral roots in search of nutrients as the plant continues to grow. In some plants, adventitious roots take off from the base or stem of the plant. (In a few plants, adventitious roots may grow from leaves that simply rest on the ground for a time.) The prop or support roots of cornstalks are adventitious, as are the roots that form on creepers from strawberry and other vines. (Fig. 5-3)

Fig. 5-3. Adventitious Peach Roots (Photo courtesy of Stark Brothers Nurseries)

Root Type

The classification of root types is related to the job each type of root does. Some provide storage, others provide anchors, etc.

Taproots: Taproots are the large and fleshy storage roots, such as the large root of radishes, turnips, and carrots. These provide food storage for the plant, and are also used as plant anchors. (Figs. 5-4, 5-5)

Fibrous roots: Fibrous roots are found in grasses, and form a fine network of intertwined roots which do a good job of holding soil in place, though their primary function is absorption of water to feed the plants. (Fig. 5-6)

Fascicled roots: Somewhat similar to taproots, these are adventitious roots instead of primary, and form large storage containers for plants such as sweet potatoes. While taproots provide a single storage root, fascicled roots tend to provide

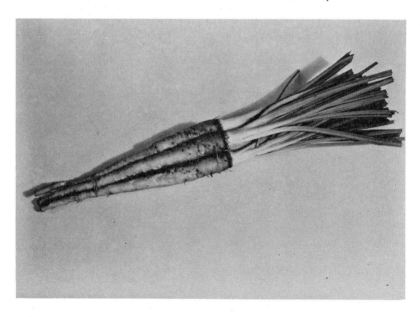

Fig. 5-4. Salsify or Oyster Plant Taproots are Plant Anchors (Photo courtesy of Burpee Seed Co.)

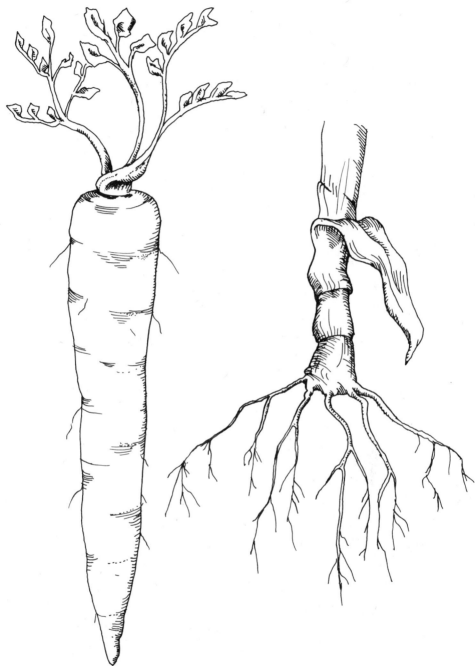

Fig. 5-5. Carrot Showing
Taproot or Storage Root

Fig. 5-6. Corn Showing
Fibrous Root System

Fig. 5-7. Adventitious Geranium Roots

several storage roots, often clumped to the stem of the plant, as in dahlias. (Fig. 5-7)

Root Functions

Roots have five functions in plant life, though there is often specialization, with different types of roots performing different functions.

Absorption: No one has yet accurately described the manner in which roots absorb water and the dissolved nutrients in soils. The process may be one of osmosis, or it may include a sort of drinking action called imbibation. (Osmosis, for those of you who remember little of your botany courses, is simply the action of water passing through a semipermeable membrane until pressure is equal on both sides of the membrane.)

Conduction: Once the root has absorbed the water, the minerals in solution in that water, and picked up oxygen from the soil, the nutrients are conducted upward to the stems, leaves, and flowers of the plant. At the same time, nutrients made in the upper parts of the plant are conducted down to the roots.

Support: Roots provide the anchorage that keeps plants from toppling over. In many cases, plants weighing a great many tons are supported by their root systems and nothing else: the nearly incomprehensible weight of the California redwood provides an excellent example. These trees may extend to 200 feet, or more, in height, and have trunks up to twelve feet in diameter. Each cubic foot of such a tree weighs about 28 pounds when dry; its living weight is quite a few pounds greater. With lifetimes of up to 1,500 years (a tree felled in 1943, in Mendocino County, had a ring count that tallied 1,728 years, with a height of 334 feet and a stump diameter of 21 feet and 4 inches!), the support of these monsters is obviously of great importance. Consider a single tree that produces 490,000 board feet of lumber; allowing for about one third in waste, that gives us a tree containing about 64,000 cubic feet. The weight of that single tree is on the order of 1,920,000 pounds if we allow only two pounds per cubic foot for additional water weight (a total of 30 pounds per cubic foot). That comes to 960 tons, all supported by the root system!

Storage: Root systems also provide storage capacity for nutrients to allow the plant to get through times of nutrient lack.

Reproduction: Vegetative reproduction is not found in all plants. Usually, a plant with a good root storage system will be more likely to present us with new plants from the root systems. In some cases, root systems for these plants go extremely deep and are hard to eradicate: the common dandelion is a good example.

While all of the nutrients taken up by the plant have some importance, usually great importance, in the over-all growth of the plant, there are a couple that help to promote great root growth and health. Nitrogen is needed to build plant proteins, and a lack of it will result in poor growth of stems and leaves, as well as poor coloring in those parts. Potassium, or potash, is absolutely essential to vigorous root growth. If potassium is not present in the soil in correct amounts, then root growth will suffer, though plant growth will suffer if other nutrients are not present also. (The most often recognized elements needed for good plant growth are nitrogen, potassium, phosphorus — essential for the setting of fruit and blossoming of flowers, sulfur, carbon, hydrogen, oxygen, iron, manganese, boron, zinc, calcium, magnesium. Of these, zinc, boron, and manganese are minor, or trace, needs.) (Fig. 5-8)

Root Growth

Root growth is dominated by the presence of water and gravity. The effect of gravity on plants is called geotropism, with root systems genetically set as positively geotropic (gravity draws them down into the soil, no matter the position in which they are sprouted), while stem growth is negatively geotropic (stems always grow up and out of the soil). A few of the branch root systems are classified as negatively geotropic. That is, they grow out to the sides, at right angles to gravity's pull, and this is believed to be genetically determined also.

Fig. 5-8. Turnip Roots Provide Nutrient Storage
(Photo courtesy of Burpee Seed Co.)

The effect of water on root growth is called hydrotropism. Again, roots are positively hydrotropic. Some water *must* be present in order that the root have an indication of direction for growth. In completely dry soil, though water may be only an inch or two away, a root will show no reaction. But allow a few drops of that water to penetrate from the source to the root, and the root will start growing toward the water source. This is a fact to consider in the watering of gardens: frequent light waterings draw the roots to the surface.

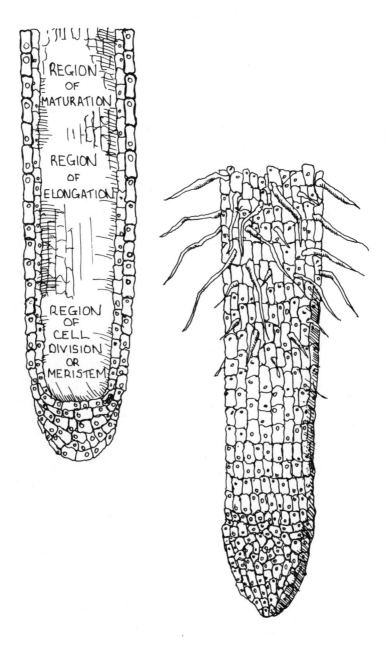

*Fig. 5-9. Enlarged
Section of Root Tip*

*Fig. 5-10. Enlarged Surface
of Root Tip Showing Root
Hairs and Root Tip*

Cell Division and Root Growth

Cell growth takes place in three ways. First, by cell division, as one cell divides into two, those two into four, and so on up the line. Second, by cell enlargement, as new cells expand to reach their full size. Third, by cell differentiation, by which cells become changed in form in order to take over their particular function in the plant. Description of the actual complex process of cell division has no real place in a book aimed mainly at gardeners, so we will not go into nucleoli, mitosis, prophase, metaphase, and anaphase.

Cell division and growth is affected strongly by temperature. Generally, we can guess that a very low temperature is going to prevent growth, while higher temperatures will enhance it. Obviously, there are limits. Few plants will grow at 150°F., though most will still do well in the occasional 100° burst. And, some plants do prefer cooler weather for maximum growth. Many conifers, such as firs and pines, are in this category. (Figs. 5-9, 5-10)

Chapter 6

PLANT PROPAGATION

Plant propagation includes root development, but need not start with roots. Because of their varied structures and jobs, roots provide a series of methods for plant propagation, with many root types needing a different method. Most vegetable and flower plants can be started quite easily from seeds, but a few require the use of layering, cuttings, or a form of compact root, either a bulb, rhizome, corm, or tuber. A technique known as division is also used, though this is, roughly, a type of cutting and will be covered there.

Cuttings

Because cutting as a method of propagation sounds much more difficult than it really is, it makes a good starting point for rooting plants. Certain advantages are inherent in cuttings as methods of starting plants. First, some plants are sterile: these are usually desirable hybrids, whose seeds are expensive. In other cases, when a plant is not necessarily sterile but still a hybrid, the offspring will not breed true to the parent plant if seeds from that parent are used. Again, such hybrid seeds tend to be somewhat expensive. Cuttings do not depend on the fertility of the parent plant seeds, nor is there any worry about a hybrid plant reverting to one of the ancestor plants with less desirable characteristics (smaller flowers, smaller vegetable yields, less resistance to disease, etc.).

The basic idea of a cutting is simply to cut off a small part of the parent plant, insert it in a rooting medium such as water, peat moss, soil or sand, and keep it reasonably moist, in good light, and warm until new roots start to form. (Fig. 6-1)

Cuttings may be taken from any of several different plant parts, including tubers, roots, rhizomes, stems, or leaves. They may also be taken from dormant or active plants. These last are often called green, or softwood, cuttings, whereas the others may be called ripe, or hardwood, cuttings. Softwood cuttings may also be taken from hardwood plants at the correct time of year, usually in early spring; hardwood cuttings are taken from growth at least a year old.

Softwood Cuttings

The decision as to when to take a softwood cutting is simply made, though a bit of practice will provide greatest accuracy. Select a freshly sprouted part of the plant, and break it off. If it gives a snap as it is broken, then the plant is ready to yield a softwood cutting. If the shoot crushes between your fingers, then the piece is too young to make a successful propagation. If it bends and doesn't snap off, then the shoot is too old.

When the proper shoot is located, take a cutting about three or four inches long, slicing straight across the base just below a joint. Cut to the bud whenever possible, as this comes closer to assuring success: roots appear to start more readily near these joints or buds. Try to get no less than three buds on each cutting. Leave a little leaf surface on the cutting, so that life processes can continue while the cutting is forming its new root system. Usually it is best to cut off any leaves at the bottom of the cutting and leave the top leaves on. On large-leafed plants, you may wish to cut the upper leaves in half to reduce water loss by transpiration.

The bed for the cuttings and the rooting medium are now of great importance. For large numbers of cuttings, build some sort of cold frame. If you are preparing only one or two, you can use pots, peat starter pots, or even the bases of milk

Fig. 6-1. Cuttings in Rootstock (Photo courtesy of Stark Brothers Nurseries)

cartons to hold the rooting medium. Select a rooting medium that will provide good drainage for the cuttings: peat moss, sand, or very fine gravel are all excellent.

Place the medium in the pot or cold frame and level it. Next, water until damp, but not drenched. (It should feel moist to a finger inserted in the medium, but should not feel soaked.) Level and pack after checking. Use a knitting needle or similar tool to make holes for the cuttings. Insert the cuttings and press them down into the holes with a gentle firmness. Pile a bit of the extra rooting medium around the cuttings so it won't tip over. Green cuttings need to get into the rooting medium as quickly as possible, and must be kept in a cool, shady spot until the insertions are made.

Place the inserted cuttings in a shady spot, and soak them with water, using a mister. Rooting will take about two weeks, during which time these cuttings must be kept warm (but not hot), allowed plenty of air circulation, and protected from direct sunlight. Misting at least once a day, until the cuttings are drenched, is also needed, since there is, as yet, no root system to take in water from the rooting medium.

Once roots reach about one-half inch in length, you can move the cuttings to two- or three-inch ceramic pots and allow a bit more light to hit them, while still keeping them out of direct sunlight. Watering should be fairly heavy during this period to promote rapid root growth.

Hardwood Cuttings

To work with cuttings that require somewhat less gentle handling at the outset, and that can be stored (with the butts buried in the soil, below the frost level and facing up), we have to move to hardwood cuttings. Again, almost all plants, whether hardwood or softwood, can be propagated from this type of cutting. Hardwood cuttings are taken from the wood of the previous season, or wood that is even older. The leaves need not be retained, though retention is possible if the cuttings are going to be used immediately. Any hardwood cutting which retains the leaves should have them trimmed down in the same manner as for softwood cuttings. Hardwood cuttings also provide a simple method of making the decision as to timing. The cutting is taken in either the spring or fall, and may be used for immediate rooting (as is often the case with spring cuttings), or held, as already mentioned, for spring use. Winter cuttings may also be taken and stored indoors in a moist, cool rooting medium. The advantage of storing cuttings over the winter is that the stored cuttings, because they form a sort of growth to protect the cut surfaces, root more easily than do immediately rooted hardwood cuttings. (For some reason, the protective surface aids in root formation, possibly because it is, at least in part, a sort of root itself.)

Hardwood cuttings are taken from bud to bud, just as are softwood types, but they are usually about twice as long as the softwood cuttings, four to eight inches. These are single season transplants when done rooting, if the actual rooting takes place in spring weather and is done outdoors (softwood cuttings cannot be rooted outdoors). You will not see roots forming in two weeks, as you will with softwood cuttings. While the actual root formation time will depend on the plant, you will usually find that hardwood cuttings take a fair amount longer to send out roots of any decent size.

Rooting medium and methods are exactly like those of softwood cuttings, though the need for protection from direct sunlight is less (it's still a good idea), and the cold frames or pots with the cuttings can be kept outdoors (assuming it is far enough into the spring season that temperatures are above 45° or 50° at night).

Leaf Cuttings

While not universally feasible, leaf cuttings can easily propagate some types of plants. The fleshy plants known as succulents, such as many types of begonia, are easily rooted this way. Cut a mature leaf from the plant, slash the leaf where the veins join (for best results, select a point where two large veins unite), lay the leaf flat on wet sand or peat moss and place pebbles or marbles on the leaf to keep it in contact with the rooting medium. From this juncture, the cutting is handled just like a softwood cutting. The result will soon be, not just roots, but a group of tiny new plants at a great many of the points of the leaf in contact with the peat moss or sand.

Air Layering

Air layering sounds as if it were some eerie process of possible use only to the most dedicated greenhouse addicts, botanists, and mad scientists. It isn't. Air layering is not only a good method of propogating woody stemmed plants, but is also a method of rescuing plants that are defoliated for one reason or another. As a definition, air layering is a method of propagating woody plants while the branches are still attached to the parent plant. (Simple layering is even easier, with the right kind of plant, as the stem is simply run through the rooting medium, whether sand, peat moss, vermiculite, and whether the rooting medium is in the same pot with the parent plant or in another. It is an excellent method of growing extra plants without spending a cent.)

The principle that lies behind layering is one of recovery from a wound. Natural processes soon start forming a scab, or new growth of wood and bark, over any wound in a branch of a plant. As the branch fights to live, the growth increases, and we find ourselves with new plants. Whether the desire is to save a defoliated plant or simply to propagate without expenditure for seed, the process itself is relatively simple, whichever of the two ways of air layering are used.

Start by selecting a stem or a branch of reasonable size. There's no need to be really touchy about the size of the branch with this method. It may be from about a half inch on up to a bit over two inches in diameter, with a length varying from as little as half a foot up to as much as two feet. Take a sharp knife and remove the bark and cambium (the green inner layer of the bark) by cutting around the circumference twice, and then making a slit to allow the bark to be peeled away. If the branch is fairly large, say over an inch and a half in diameter, allow about one and a half inches between the circumferential cuts. Smaller branches should have the cuts about an inch apart.

Once the bark and cambium are removed, you've cut off the life flow of the plant to that branch, as there can now be no flow of sap. The branch out in front of the cuts will soon die if left uncovered. To prevent this, take a healthy handful of sphagnum moss, moisten it well, and tie it around the cut area. Taper the ends, leaving a bulge in the middle, and cover the moss with clear or translucent plastic, tied loosely at the top and tightly at the bottom.

Roots will take from one to two months to reach proper potting size, at least two inches long. Then use either a saw or a very sharp pruning shears to sever the branch. Make sure the tool is very clean, and cut just below the bottom of the sphagnum moss. Potting should follow immediately. Start by removing the moss and soaking the newly formed roots in lukewarm water. Prune back the air-layered branch until it is from six to eight inches long. Pruning cuts down on the moisture and nutrient needs of the plant, thus allowing the roots to feed the new plant more easily.

Set the rooted branch into a pot of the proper size containing a good rooting medium (sphagnum moss, vermiculite, etc.). or, better yet, good potting or garden soil. Keep the soil damp and the branch shaded for at least three months, at which time almost any plant will be ready to be placed in whatever spot you've set up as home for it.

For smaller plants (the above is especially handy when propagating trees and large shrubs), the British method works best, but requires a bit more precision than does our first style. First of all, the twig selected should be no larger in diameter than a pencil. Take a very sharp knife, and no more than a foot from the end of the branch, make an incision. Cut the twig about halfway through, carrying the cut about two inches up the twig. Best results will occur when there is a dormant bud just above the top of the cut.

Using care not to snap the twig, bend the incision until it opens enough for you to insert a pebble or a small chunk of moss. This ensures that the wound cannot close up and refuse to send out roots for you. Using sphagnum moss in the same manner as with the first type of air layering, place a good handful around the wound, making certain it is well moistened, though not dripping wet. Again, a plastic cover is needed, with the top tied loosely and the bottom tightly. If this cover isn't tied properly, the rooting medium will dry out much too rapidly, and the branch tip will simply die without any roots forming.

With the British method of air layering, roots should form more quickly, with most being ready for potting after about one month, though a few plant varieties may require up to six weeks to present you with roots a couple of inches long. When you remove the cover to check on root growth, attend to getting it re-tied as close to the original style as possible to prevent drying out.

Potting is done in the manner described for the first type of air layering.

House Plants and Air Layering

A few house plants can be successfully air layered, most especially those which have slender, long stems, such as rubber plants, philodendrons, and oleander. The methods are essentially similar to method two, as described above, with the exception of a need for a stake to support the air-layered section of the house plant. (The stems of these plants are not often strong enough to support the extra weight of the moss, the ties, and the plastic cover.)

Cut the stem near the leafy top of the plant, slicing about halfway through the stalk and carrying the cut a bit up toward the leaves, though no more than about one inch (this will vary according to the thickness of the stem). Prop the cut open, encircle it with moistened sphagnum moss, and wrap the moss, as before, with plastic. In one and a half or two months, the roots will be developed to the point where potting is possible, using either packaged potting soil or a mixture of about a third peat moss, a third compost, and a final third of sharp sand.

New root length will differ with the plant variety, so if you are unsure whether or not they're strong enough to support the new plant, simply allow the time to extend to eight weeks, Then go ahead with your potting.

Ground, or Simple, Layering

All forms of layering require a modest investment of time by the gardener, usually no more than ten minutes or so, after which little other than a bit of patience is needed to have a new plant form that is ready for potting or setting out. Ground layering cuts even this time investment, though the need for patience is increased, since many outdoor plants will take as long as two growing seasons to send out a root system strong enough to allow transplanting.

For ground layering, select only well established plants, of course. You will be limited here in the selection, since only those varieties that direct at least some branches or shoots downward to where they can be easily bent to reach the ground are usable. In early spring, March or April depending on ground temperatures in your area, select a shoot or branch growing close enough down to reach the ground easily. A shoot with growth from the previous year is best, since it will form roots most rapidly, but even old branches will form roots eventually. Make a cut about one and a half or two inches long at the point you wish to have the roots form. Slant the cut up and to the center of the branch, and prop the cut open with a pebble, if necessary to hold it open when you bury it.

Now bend the branch down and insert the cut portion gently into a hole about six inches deep, with the tip of the sliced portion pointing down. Make any bends gently enough to prevent snapping the branch. You can use wooden pegs, wire, or stones to hold the branch in position. Make sure at least half a foot of the portion of the branch beyond the cut extends above the surface, and gently tamp the earth back around the cut portion. Moisten. At this point, you can add a layer of mulch (making sure that the six inches you allowed for above-surface area still extends above the mulch) to cut down on watering needs, or you can simply check every few days to make sure that the layered portion is kept moist all through the growing season.

During the second growing season, the plant should have produced a strong enough root system to withstand being cut away from the parent plant and transplanted to a shady area. The first year, shade should be maintained, and the plants must be well watered. After that, they can be permanently set out.

Incidentally, the severing from the parent plant is best done at the *end* of the second growing season, as the plant becomes dormant.

Rhizomes

In many houseplants and a variety of other plants, rhizomes can be used to form cuttings that will root quite easily. A rhizome is nothing more than an underground stem, sections of which will contain leaf buds. If you have a plant that forms these growths, all that is necessary is to cut the rhizomes into sections, each containing a leaf bud, and pot them in a good rooting medium. These will quite quickly, if kept moist and shaded, develop new root systems and thence plants.

Tubers

Most of us are familar with potatoes. They are archetypical tubers. Plants such as the Jerusalem artichoke, which also form thick, fleshy underground storage roots with eyes, are also tubers. But not all storage, or tuberous, roots are classified as tubers. If the root doesn't grow "eyes" it is not a tuber, and cannot be propagated as one. To get tubers to reproduce, all you need to do is to cut the root into sections, each section containing an eye.

Using potatoes as an example, it is easy to state that planting each of the tuber sections containing an "eye" will then provide you with a number of plants, each producing a good yield of this vegetable. But it's not always that simple. For a long time potatoes were considered a good crop only in those areas where summer heat did not become too intense.

Today, the use of deep mulches has cut down on the need for moderate summers to produce potatoes, but it must be remembered that potatoes will wither and die in strong heat. In fact, it isn't always essential to plant potatoes in the ground. Many gardeners now place the pieces of tuber on the surface of the ground, and then cover them with about a foot to eighteen inches of straw mulch. To use this method, all you need do is make sure the ground is fertile and acid (potatoes grow best with a pH of 5.0 to 6.0). Place the tuber pieces on the ground, mulch, and keep an eye on them. If, before harvest time, the potatoes show through the mulch, simply add another few inches of hay or straw.

The simplicity of this method is great. It saves making drills five to six inches deep for each "eye," and saves you digging the potatoes out when harvest time comes. Simply pull back the mulch and place the potatoes in a basket or sack.

If you wish early potatoes, you can harvest whenever they have reached the correct size. For best long-term storage, though, let most of the potatoes reach maturity. You can easily tell when potato plants are ready for harvest by looking at their tops: withered tops mean mature potatoes. Store tubers in a dark place to prevent their greening. If potatoes do green, throw them out, as they are not fit for consumption and may actually cause illness.

For a tuber that is completely starch-free, you may wish to try the Jerusalem artichoke. Though an artichoke, this variety is not related strongly to the common globe artichoke. It is a member of the sunflower family with the features of a tuber. Some of the plants can reach a height of more than ten feet, and the plant has a tendency to spread rapidly, so that in a few gardens it can become as much of a nuisance as a help.

Use basically the same methods of planting seed or "eye" sections of the tuber as you would with potatoes, but keep in mind the great height of the plants. Set in the wrong spot, artichokes will screen plants that may need a great deal of sunlight.

This artichoke doesn't keep well indoors, and it must be kept moist (actually damp) to prevent shriveling of the skin. Leave them in the ground and dig as needed, for the plant is completely immune to the effects of frost (or at least the tuber is).

Bulbs

As far as the vegetable garden is concerned, the onion group

is the major type of bulb plant. This includes such diverse
plants as chives, leeks, shallots, garlic, and onions. Climate
matters little to these plants, but the ground must be in a state
of fine tilth: tightly packed earth will cut down on growth
and cause you to have misshapen vegetables.

Chives may be grown as a border around other garden vegetables, but will work just as well planted in rows. Because we
use only the stems or stalks of the chive plant, they can be
classified as a perennial, and should be planted in areas where
they can remain without disturbance for several years. If left
in one spot for more than a couple of years, though, some of
the plants will need to be divided and planted elsewhere.
Chives are prolific and will soon become too thickly clumped
for best growth.

Onions come in many varieties, and do best in temperate
climates, though they can be grown nearly anywhere. Seed-
sown onions are seldom a good idea for the home gardener, as
they are the least certain of the three methods of planting.
Instead, onion sets are used. These are small, dry onions, best
when under 3/4 of an inch in size, that were grown the previous year. These work well in any garden. Seedlings are small
green plants. The cost is about the same as for sets, as is planting ease. (Fig. 6-2)

Shallots are really small onions, with a less intense flavor.
They can be planted as most onions are, and left in the ground
from year to year. Larger crops will form if the bulbs are tak-
en from the ground each year and the smaller ones replanted
in the spring.

Garlic is planted by dividing the bulbs into small cloves, as
if you were getting ready to season a sauce, and planting each
clove, separately. Take care with garlic to prevent freezing.
In the South, get the garlic into a cool, dry place quickly to
prevent spoiling from heat and excess moisture. Again, as
with all bulb plants, tilth of the soil must be good and loose.

Leeks are onionlike plants, but instead of forming a large bulb, they produce thick, fleshy leaves. They are used much as are onions. Generally, leeks are grown best from seed, in soil with good tilth. Sow the seeds in a shallow trench, then, as the plants grow, hill the earth up around the plants. With good tilth and good growing conditions, leeks will reach an inch and a half in diameter, with white sections half a foot or more long. Store in a cool, dry place.

Flowers from Bulbs

Flowers that grow from bulbs have two attractions. First, bulbs produce some of the most beautiful varieties of flowers; and second, they are among the earliest varieties to flower. (The crocuses may well pop right up through a snow cover.)

Growing bulb flowers is one of the simpler gardening jobs. (In this discussion of bulb flowers, we include rhizomes, tubers, and corms, such as the dahlia and the crocus.) Check the bulbs, first, for condition. They will have smooth, and a bit shiny, skins, free of damage of any kind. Reject any that have cuts and bruises. Expect also to receive an impression of weight in comparison to the size of the bulb: the heavier the bulb for its size, the more likely it is to produce a strong plant.

Bulbs are planted at different times, and they should be bought just before planting. Loosen up the soil to a bit more than planting depth. Follow the chart below for planting times and depths for some of the most popular bulbs. In areas of the deep South, you will need to modify the schedule. First, add four inches to the depth of planting. Keep the planting to at least partial shade, while avoiding deep shade through the entire day. Plant no earlier than the beginning of October, with preference given to a month or so later in the warmest areas. Water the plantings often.

Plant	Planting Time	Flowering	Planting Depth
Crocus	Sept. 1 to Dec. 1	March 15 to March 30	3"
Daffodil, all sizes	Sept. 1 to Dec. 1	April 10 to April 25	6"
Tulip, early	Sept. 15 to Dec. 15	April 15 to April 30	6"
Tulip, later	Sept. 15 to Dec. 15	May 5 to May 20	5" to 6"
Hyacinth	Sept. 15 to Dec. 15	April 15 to April 30	6"

For best year-to-year results, a certain amount of care must be given to bulbs after the first planting. Of course, the earth should be kept fertile, but during the bulbs' dormant stages, you should mulch so that frost heave cannot shift the bulbs to the surface where they would be subject to frost damage. Remove the mulch as soon as spring arrives so that the ground can warm up.

Once the flowers on the plants start to fade, they should be clipped and removed. The root system won't have to work to keep them alive, thus depriving itself of time for storage of nutrients to get through the winter.

Bulbs are most easily planted by simply using a trowel to reach the correct depth, inserting the bulb, covering, and watering. Other methods add complexity without much increasing growth, though you may find it easier to use a dipper or bulb planter. (Fig. 6-3)

Since bulbs can also be easily and successfully grown indoors, these flowers provide more than ordinary versatility. In fact, hyacinths can be grown indoors without soil. Special

hyacinth glasses are used for this. Check with the dealer sell-
ing the varieties you prefer to see if they are suited to growth
in glass. Then fill a glass with about one third charcoal and
top with water. Set the bulb so that its base just touches the
water.

Next, place the bulb in a cool dark spot for about two
months, or until root formation and young plant growth is
good (leaf growth should reach about an inch and a half by
this time). Add water to keep the glass full, and place it in
strong light after ten days or so of modest light. This tends to
be enjoyable while also providing a fair amount of information on the development of root systems, and will, if done
properly, produce a vigorous and attractive plant.

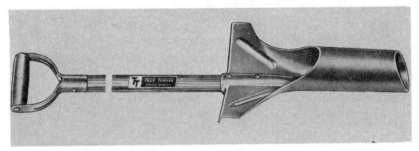

Fig. 6-3. Bulb Planter (Photo Courtesy of True Temper)

Root Crop Vegetables

We have covered the tuberous varieties of vegetables, but root
crops don't come close to ending there. Storage root types
have for a long, long time provided us with the many kinds of
vegetables that are stored to prevent starvation when the growing season ends. In fact, without such crops we can be sure
that even larger segments of humanity would have starved to
death over the centuries.

Beets provide an easily grown crop. They are not overly
sensitive to extreme heat, and need only protection from freez-

ing during extreme northern winters. Beet seed — which comes in small balls, each ball containing several seeds — is planted to a depth of about one inch. Successive plantings will provide young beets during the growing season, with enough left to mature fully for winter storage at the end of the season. To prevent damage to the root, beets should be harvested before heavy frost. Pull the beets from the ground, then cut the tops about one inch above the top of the root (cutting down to the root will allow the beet to bleed). Keep storage temperatures just above freezing (about 35°F.), and you can reasonably expect beets to stay edible for four months, possibly even five. Since the beets need some moisture to keep from shriveling, the best storage procedure is to place the beets in boxes filled with moist sand or with hay that is moistened occasionally. Sand is best, as hay kept moist for long periods has a tendency to develop rot, which may then be passed on to the beets.

Dennis the Menace may not care for carrots, but most people do. This vegetable is an important one for storage, since it is one of the few root vegetables having a heavy supply of vitamin A. The varieties with the greatest amounts are those with the deepest orange colors; pale carrots contain a great deal less. Again, soil with good tilth is needed. Seeding can be done early in the spring, as carrots of almost all varieties are quite hardy. Seed as early as you can work the ground, covering the seed with from a quarter to a half inch of soil (the lighter the soil, the deeper the coverage). Thin to no more than about ten or a dozen plants per foot in the row. Because carrot seeds are so tiny, a lot of thinning may be needed if they're put directly into the soil. To keep seed waste down, simply mix about a quarter ounce of seed, thoroughly, with a cup of clean, dry sand. This mixture should provide sufficient seed for a fifty-foot row of carrots. If thinning is still needed, pull the young carrots and use them in salads or as garnishes.

Carrots can be stored at the same temperature as are beets, again keeping the moisture content high by using either sand or straw. (Fig. 6-4)

Fig. 6-2. One Variety of Onion Bulb (Photo courtesy of Burpee Seed Co.)

Fig. 6-4. Carrots, Rich in Vitamin A (Photo courtesy of Burpee Seed Co.)

Fig. 6-5. Quick-maturing Red Radishes (Photo courtesy of Burpee Seed Co.)

Fig. 6-6. Winter Radishes for Storage (Photo courtesy of Burpee Seed Co.)

Chervil, turnip-rooted style, is a crop that winters over in much of the United States. The seeds are sown in the fall, the plants grow in the spring. Generally, planting and spacing are about the same as for carrots, as is winter storage.

Parsnips need a light, friable soil, and the seed should be sown thickly, with later thinning providing plants some three inches apart. Sowing is done as early in the spring as the ground can be worked. The roots need not be taken from the ground for indoor storage. In fact, many people claim that freezing is good for parsnips, imparting a more delicate flavor to the root. Once new tops start to grow in the spring, though, the previous year's crop should be immediately harvested, because the roots will tend to become quite lean and almost soggy tasting.

Radishes are the little garnishers that everyone seems to love. Germination and growth are exceptionally rapid, with many varieties being mature within about three weeks of planting. Soil conditioning needs are minimal. As long as the soil is friable, radishes will grow. Still, for best flavor, quick growth is needed, so a fertile soil is best. (Fig. 6-5)

Two basic types are to be found, though there are many, many varieties of each type: the small, red, globular radishes and the strong winter varieties. The latter can require up to two and a half months to reach maturity. Winter radishes are planted and stored just as are other root crops, while the quick-maturing varieties should be used quickly, because taste deteriorates rapidly. (Fig. 6-6)

Turnips and rutabaga are cool season root crops that grow best in northerly areas, but will do well in most of the United States. Turnips will do better below northern Virginia than will rutabagas. Turnips reach full size in about eighty days, whereas rutabagas may need a month longer to attain maturity. In northerly areas, turnips should be seeded in July or August; in the South the best results come from winter or spring seedings. Seeds should be covered only lightly, and an eye kept on the roots after about sixty days. Turnips that grow too large become woody and have a bitter taste. For best storage and flavor, harvest before the first frost whenever possible. Winter storage follows the procedures recommended for most other root crop vegetables, such as beets and carrots.

Chapter 7

ROOT SYSTEM PROBLEMS

Like all parts of all plants, root systems, no matter the kind, are subject to damage from a variety of insects, diseases, and soil conditions. We have already covered the types of soil and ways to improve them. Now it is time to look at those other things, big and small, that can damage your plant's root system.

Diseases

While most human diseases seem to be caused by bacteria, many plant diseases are the result of fungi of parasitic bent. Any part of the plant is subject to diseases, and there are many kinds that will attack any portion that is vulnerable. Plants have an epidermis, just as do human beings, and this outer layer is resistant to diseases. Much plant disease, then, results from damage to this skin layer which allows the entrance of parasites into the more vulnerable inner layers. The snapping off of a few root hairs during cultivation may be enough to allow disease-producing organisms to enter the plant.

After that, you will begin to see the signs of the particular disease. Of course, damping off, a fungus disease of seedlings, is probably the first sign of dire problems. When growing or mature plants begin to turn yellow and wilt, the disease is present. (This, of course, is not the case when potato plants wilt after maturity, for that is a sign of harvest time.)

One of the major causes, around the middle of the growing season, of the premature death of some plants, among them tomatoes, all root crops, and melons, is a disease called "root knots." These distorted roots, many with large swellings, are caused by nematodes.

Wilt diseases also include those in which the outer surface of the roots appears healthy, but when the epidermis is removed from either stems or roots, a discoloration, brown and much wetter than normal, can be found. Fungi or bacteria may be the cause of the disease, depending on the plant. The greatest destructive effects are found on tomatoes, potatoes, cabbages, beans, cucumbers, peas, and sweet potatoes. Fortunately for gardeners, these wilt disease parasites are each single-crop demons. That is, you can prevent the yearly destruction of crops, in most cases, simply by planting a different crop in the disease-producing area the next year, for each parasite can attack only a single type of plant.

In fact, crop rotation is a good way to keep such parasites from proliferating. If a single crop is planted in the same area year after year, the parasites will eventually be attracted to it. Rotating crops will pretty much prevent intensive buildups of disease-causing organisms.

Root-rot disease can produce one of two types of dead or decayed roots. In the first, the roots will die, but will send to

Fig. 7-1. Peach Seedlings for Transplanting
(Photo courtesy of Stark Brothers Nurseries)

the surface a brown, hairy fungus growth; in the second, the roots will turn black and have a foul odor. In the case of black root rot, the soil contains too much water, and this suffocates the roots by cutting off their ground air supply.

Most plant diseases can be prevented by providing properly drained soil in good condition and by making sure that seeds and seedlings are in good condition. For the first, we leave it to you to follow the steps described earlier in this book. For the second, you have two choices. Select seed and seedlings for transplant from reputable nurseries only. Or grow your own seedlings for transplanting. The reputation of a nursery is of exceptional importance when transplants are being purchased, as most diseases cannot be discovered at the time a plant is ready to be put out. It is only later that you learn you either bought a diseased plant ot set it into poor soil conditions. (Fig. 7-1)

Keeping a garden weed-free is another excellent idea, for many varieties of weeds carry organisms inimical to the health of garden plants, as well as providing competition for soil nutrients.

Never allow the garden to continue saturated, if possible. In periods of exceptionally heavy rain, you may find it necessary to construct some kind of drainage ditching around the garden. Or you may even have to give up until the following year and use a higher and better-drained location for your garden.

Practice isolation. When a plant shows signs of disease, remove any diseased portions and get them out of the garden.

Keep a check on soil requirements for the plants you are growing, and keep a close eye, with monthly tests, if necessary, on the pH of the soil. For example, consider potatoes. With a pH preference of 5.0 to 6.0, potatoes obviously require an acid soil. But one disease, potato scab, has been proven to be a lot less active when the soil pH is closer to 5.2 or even lower than when it is up near 6.0.

For those plants which may have such needs, or preferences, I would recommend you check with a county extension agent. In most cases, these people will have up-to-date lists showing soil preferences. They will also be able to supply you with a strong indication of which diseases are most likely to hit your area, no matter the kind of gardening you're doing. One of

the more important ways to fight disease is to use plants resistant to the diseases found in a locale. The extension agent
will not only be able to tell you the diseases most likely to
hit your plants, but will have up-to-date lists of the most resistant varieties of plants on the market. Diseases crop up in
new areas all the time, while many new strains of old diseases,
and just plain new diseases, will develop as time passes, par- ·
ticularly as more and more people begin to plant gardens.
For this reason, it is impossible to list here the diseases which
might befall a crop anywhere. Thus a check with a local ex-
pert becomes essential.

Insects

Insects not only outnumber man on this planet, but by some
estimates, outweigh him. There are many varieties, some harmless, many harmful, and many helpful. Generally, an insect
at maturity will have six legs, three pair, and a body divided
into three main parts, a head, a thorax, and an abdomen. They
will have an exoskeleton; that is, their skeleton will be on the
exterior of the body, instead of, as is ours, on the interior.
Here we are concerned only with the variety of insects known
as pests, but it still will pay to keep in mind that often broad-
spectrum insecticides are not wisely used, for those cause good,
as well as pestilential, insect life to cease.

There are several methods of insect control, with the simplest often being the purchase of resistant varieties of plants
or seeds. Again, the county extension agent will be able to
assist you in making your selection.

Isolation or removal is the next step. If a plant is diseased
or insect-ridden, get it out of the garden. Don't keep it around
to show others in the hope you can find out what is wrong

and "cure" it, for that is simply an excellent method of spreading whatever disease or insect is doing the damage. Destroy affected plants as soon as problems are apparent.

The most drastic step to take against insects is their destruction. While organic gardeners are likely to use more or less harmless methods of doing this, most of today's gardeners do not follow, at least not totally, organic precepts. In such cases, too many gardeners will go to strong, widely effective, insecticides, with the result being the destruction of virtually all insects in the garden, as well as possibly passing the poisons used on in the food chain by contaminating the vegetables or fruit, and having the poisons picked up by birds who eat insects.

If insecticides are used, it is best to use the varieties of insecticide that dissipate rapidly. Again, these substances come and go from the market, if not rapidly, at least frequently, so the recommendations of a concerned county agent will provide a guide that will be continually up to date.

In other cases, you can use organic gardening methods such as the introduction of insects inimical to those destroying your garden. Ladybugs are a good example; they are well known to almost everyone, and are commonly available in pint and quart volumes. Wasps will destroy a great many plant-harming insects, and the praying mantis, again easily available commercially, will eliminate a great many. This form of biological control can cause little damage to any environment, and it is effective in a great many instances.

Japanese beetles are a gardener's *bête noir* in too many instances. First introduced into the United States, by accident, back in 1916, this miserable little insect rapidly became, and has remained, a prolific and damaging enemy of gardeners and farmers. Originally, the United States did not have the bacterial organisms which control this beetle naturally in its homeland.

You can check with your local agricultural agent for availability of the control known as milky spore disease. This disease attacks the beetle grubs, while the disease remains in the soil to provide a cumulative effect, thus assuring you of a continuing treatment on your land. Not only is this treatment long term, but it is harmless to other insects, human beings, and plants, and is not affected by weather.

Application is simplicity itself. About a teaspoonful is applied directly to the grass, soil, or sod in spots some four feet apart, at any time when the ground is not frozen and the wind too high. Various agricultural groups agree that the Japanese beetle kill rate approaches 90° percent overall.

Other insects may require other techniques. In some cases, traps will work, though these tend to be as indiscriminate as insecticides in killing harmless and helpful insects as well as the pests.

Generally, diseases and insects of the harmful type won't become prevalent in a garden if good basic soil care and sanitation techniques are followed. Thus, if your garden is in shape to provide a plant with a healthy root system, and the plant itself is of the correct variety and in good condition, you should have little problem in raising a good garden. If instead, you leave piles of garden trash lying around, don't bother to weed, and place the garden in an area where water can stand, then you will have a lot of trouble raising a decent crop.

In most cases, a good garden requires only a little more work and thought than does a poor garden. The differences, for the effort, can be outstanding. It pays to pay attention to soils, roots, and their needs.

INDEX

absorption, 69
acidity, 10, 24, 38
acid soils, 24, 47, 97
acre-foot, 9
actinomycenes, 9
adobe soils, 18
adventitious roots, 65
aeration, 10, 12, 56
aeration posts, 49
agricultural agent, 14, 23, 24
air layering, 79-82
  British method, 80-81
  house plants, 81-82
algae, 9
alkaline deposits, 5
alkaline soils, 24, 28
alkalinity, 10, 24, 46
aluminum, 3, 19, 21
ammonia, 9
anaerobic organisms, 9
aspidistra, 24

bacteria, 6, 8-9, 32, 94, 95
bark, 50, 79, 80
bean, 95
beets, 89-90, 93
  beet seed, 90
begonia, 78
black plastic, 56
blueberries, 24
bog soils, 18
bonemeal, 37
bones, 50
boron, 70
bulb planter, 88

bulbs, 74, 85-89
  flowers from bulbs, 87-89
burlap, 49

cabbage, 95
calcium, 19, 21, 22, 24, 34, 70
calcium carbonate, 37
California redwood, 69-70
caliche layer, 5
cambrium, 79, 80
capillary water, 5
carbon, 3, 70
carbon dioxide, 5, 6, 9, 16
carrots, 90, 92, 93
cart, 61
castings, 8
cell differentiation, 73
cell division, 73
cell enlargement, 73
ceramic pots, 77
chalk, 37
chernozem soils, 19-21
chervil, 92
chestnut and brown soils, 18
chives, 86
chlorophyll, 9
clay, 11, 14
clayey soils, 11, 12, 37, 58
clay hardpan, 4, 5
cold frame, 76, 78
color density, 27
common hoe, 61
compost, 46, 47-54, 56, 58, 82
  additions, 53
  capping, 53

components, 49-51
making, 48-49
pit, 48, 49
quick composting, 53-54
sheet composting, 54, 58
turning, 53, 54
watering, 51
winter composting, 48, 49
concrete blocks, 48, 49
conduction, 69
conifers, 73
copper, 3
corm, 74, 87
corncobs, 51
county extension agent, 97,
98, 99, 100
cranberries, 24
crocus, 87
crop rotation, 95
cucumber, 95
cultivation, 58-60, 94
cuttings, 74-79
hardwood, 75, 77-78
leaf, 78-79
softwood, 75-77, 78, 79
winter, 77-78

dahlia, 87
damping off, 95
Darwin, Charles, 8
desert soils, 17-18
dipper, 88
diseases, 94-98, 99
damping off, 95
potato scab, 97
root knots, 95
root-rot, 95
wilt diseases, 95
dolomitic limes, 34

drainage ditching, 97

earthworms, 6-8, 51
eggshells, 50
electron microscope, 8
enzymatic system, 8
epidermis, 94, 95
eye sections, 84, 85

fascicled roots, 66
fats, 50
fence posts, 39
fertilizer, 23, 29, 47, 50
fibrous roots, 66
filter paper, 27, 28
flowers from bulbs, 87-89
planting times, 88
food chain, 99
forage plants, 54
friability, 12, 92
fungi, 9, 94, 95

garbage, 50
garden hose, 61-62
garden tools, 60-62
garden tractor, 62
garden trimmings, 50
garlic, 86
geotropism, 71
globe artichoke, 85
granite dust, 53
grass clippings, 49, 50, 55, 56
gravel, 11, 14
gravitational water, 4
gravity, 71
green manuring, 54
ground layering, 82-83

gypsum, 37

hand tilling, 58
hardwood cuttings, 75, 77-78
hay, 50, 55, 56, 84, 90
hay mulch, 46
humus, 6, 10, 11, 17, 18, 19,
    46, 47, 55, 59
hyacinth, 88-89
hybrids, 74, 75
hydrated lime, 37
hydrate of lime, 37
hydrogen, 3, 70
hydrogen ions, 24
hydrotropism, 71
hygroscopic water, 5

imbibation, 69
inert rock fragments, 14
inorganic material, 6
insecticides, 98, 99
insects, 94, 98-100
    Japanese beetles, 99-100
    ladybugs, 99
    milky spore disease, 100
    praying mantis, 99
    wasps, 99
iodine, 3
iron, 3, 11, 19, 21, 70
iron oxide, 19
isolation, 97, 98-99

Japanese beetles, 99-100
Jerusalem artichoke, 84, 85

ladybugs, 99
lateral roots, 65
laterite soils, 19
laterization, 19

lawnmower, 54, 62
leaching, 4, 17, 19, 24, 25, 37,
    54, 58
leaf cuttings, 78-79
leather scraps, 51
leaves, 47, 50, 53, 56, 77
leeks, 86, 87
lime, 5, 19, 21, 34, 37, 47, 53
    dolomitic limes, 34
limestone, 19, 37
loamy soils, 11, 12-14

magnesium, 3, 16, 34, 70
manganese, 70
manure, 49, 50, 51, 53
marble, 37, 78
mason's cord, 61
melon, 95
mesh screen, 58
microbes, 16
microorganisms, 8-10, 32, 48, 51
microscope, 8
milky spore disease, 100
mister, 77
moisture, 10
mulch, 32, 46, 50, 55-58, 59, 60,
    83, 84, 88
    benefits, 58
    ingredients, 56-57
    time, 57

negative geotropism, 71
nematodes, 95
newspapers, 56
night air temperature, 32
night soil temperature, 32
nitrate, 9, 10
nitrite, 9
nitrogen, 3, 9, 23, 37, 39, 51,
    54, 56, 70

nitrogen deficiency testing, 27
nitrogen sulfate, 10
nursery, 97
nutrients, 5, 6, 8, 9, 22, 23, 37,
    47, 54, 57, 58, 65, 69, 70,
    80, 97

oleander, 81
onion, 85, 86
organic gardening, 99
organic matter, 6, 9, 16, 18,
    46, 48, 55, 58, 59
osmosis, 69
oxygen, 3, 5, 6, 69, 70
oyster shells, 37

parasites, 94, 95
parsnips, 92
pea, 95
peat moss, 56, 75, 78, 79, 82
peat soils, see bog soils
peat starter pots, 76
pebbles, 78
peds, 14
percentage of deficiency, 23
perennial, 86
pH, 10, 23, 24, 26-27,
    30-31, 34-37, 97
    balancing, 34-37
    scale, 47
    tests, 26-27
phages, 9
philodendron, 81
phosphate, 19
phosphorus, 37, 51, 70
phosphorus content, 23
phosphorus deficiency
    testing, 27-28
pitcherplant, 24
pitchfork, 53

plant propagation, 74-93
    air layering, 79-82
    bulbs, 85-89
    cuttings, 74-79
    ground layering, 82-83
    rhizomes, 83-84
    root crop vegetables, 89-93
    tubers, 84-85
plastic, 56, 80, 81, 82
    black, 56
podzolic soils, 18-19, 21
positive geotropism, 71
posthole digger, 26
potash, see potassium
potassium, 3, 23, 29, 70
potassium testing, 28-29
potato, 46, 57, 84, 85, 95, 97
potato scab, 97
potting soil, 80, 82
prairie grasses, 17, 18
prairie soils, 17, 18
praying mantis, 99
precipitation, 4
primary roots, 65
protozoa, 9
pruning shears, 80

quick composting, 53-54
quicklime, see lime

radishes, 92
rendzina soils, 18
reproduction, 70
rhizomes, 74, 75, 83-84, 87
root crop vegetables, 89-93
    beets, 89-90, 93
    carrots, 90, 92, 93
    chervil, 92
    parsnips, 92
    radishes, 92

rutabaga, 92-93
turnips, 92-93
root hairs, 63, 65, 94
rooting medium, 75, 76, 77, 78, 79, 81, 84
root knots, 95
root-rot, 95
roots, 63-73, 75, 78, 80, 93
  adventitious, 65
  cell growth, 73
  fascicled, 66
  fibrous, 66
  formation, 65
  function, 69-70, 78
  growth, 70-71
  lateral, 65
  primary, 65
  secondary, 65
  taproots, 66
  type, 66-69
root system problems, 94-100
  diseases, 94-98, 99
  insects, 94, 98-100
rotary tilling, 58, 59, 62
rubber plant, 81
rutabaga, 92-93
Ruth Stout No-Work Garden Book, The, 55

saline deposits, 3
sand, 11, 14, 75, 78, 79, 82, 90
sandy soils, 11-12, 14, 34, 37, 46, 58
sap, 80
saw, 80
sawdust, 47, 50, 51, 56
scab, 79
secondary roots, 65
second growing season, 83
seedlings, 94, 96

serial tests, 25
sewage sludge, 49, 50
shallots, 86
sheet composting, 54, 58
silicon, 3, 19
silt, 11, 14
simple layering, 79
single season transplant, 78
slaked lime, *see* hydrate of lime
soapy water, 50
sodium, 3, 16
softwood cuttings, 75-77, 78, 79
soil, 3-16, 17-22, 23-29, 32-62
  care, 32-62
  characteristics, 10-11
  classification, 17-22
  development, 16
  environment, 9-10
  gases, 5-7
  microorganisms, 8-10
  minerals, 3
  organic material, 6, 9
  samples, 25-26
  structure, 14-16
  temperature, 32-34
  tests, 23-29
  texture, 11-14
  water, 4-5
soil color, 10-11
soil water, 3-5
spade shovel, 58, 61
spading fork, 58
sphagnum moss, 80, 81, 82
steel bow rake, 61
storage (root), 70
Stout, Ruth, 55, 57
straw, 55, 56, 84, 90
succulents, 78
Sudbury Soil Test kit, 25

sulfides,   10
sulfur,   70
support (root),   69
sweet potato,   95

taproots,   66
tap water,   3
tilling,   58-60
tilth,   86, 87, 90
tomato,   95
topsoil,   53
trace elements,   3
transpiration,   34
transplanted stock,   57
trowel,   88
tuber,   46, 74, 75, 84-85,
      87, 89
tundra,   21
turnips,   92-93

vegetable crops,   24, 46
vegetable waste,   51
vermiculite,   79, 80
viruses,   9
vitamin A,   90

wasps,   99
watering,   34, 60
weeds,   97
wheelbarrow,   61
wilt diseases,   95
wilting,   34
winter composting,   48, 49
winter cuttings,   77-78
wood ash,   37, 53
wood chips,   47, 50
woody stemmed plants,   79

zinc,   3, 70
zone of saturation,   4, 5